THROUGH
THEIR EYES

THE SOUTH EAST

Edited By Elle Berry

First published in Great Britain in 2020 by:

Young Writers
Remus House
Coltsfoot Drive
Peterborough
PE2 9BF
Telephone: 01733 890066
Website: www.youngwriters.co.uk

Printed and bound in the UK by BookPrintingUK
Website: www.bookprintinguk.com
YB0428J

FOREWORD

Since 1991, here at Young Writers we have celebrated the awesome power of creative writing, especially in young adults, where it can serve as a vital method of expressing strong (and sometimes difficult) emotions, a conduit to develop empathy, and a safe, non-judgemental place to explore one's own place in the world. With every poem we see the effort and thought that each pupil published in this book has put into their work and by creating this anthology we hope to encourage them further with the ultimate goal of sparking a life-long love of writing.

Through Their Eyes challenged young writers to open their minds and pen bold, powerful poems from the points-of-view of any person or concept they could imagine – from celebrities and politicians to animals and inanimate objects, or even just to give us a glimpse of the world as they experience it. The result is this fierce collection of poetry that by turns questions injustice, imagines the innermost thoughts of influential figures or simply has fun.

The nature of the topic means that contentious or controversial figures may have been chosen as the narrators, and as such some poems may contain views or thoughts that, although may represent those of the person being written about, by no means reflect the opinions or feelings of either the author or us here at Young Writers.

We encourage young writers to express themselves and address subjects that matter to them, which sometimes means writing about sensitive or difficult topics. If you have been affected by any issues raised in this book, details on where to find help can be found at *www.youngwriters.co.uk/info/other/contact-lines*

CONTENTS

Cameron Boydcamps (11)	92
Max Lloyd (11)	93
Harry Paul Lockyer (11)	94
Alessia Pavone (17)	95

Chislehurst School For Girls, Chislehurst

Nana Agyeiwaa (14)	96
Nicolette Brown-Mason (13)	98
Carrie Giannopoulos (13)	100
Piper Lauder (13)	102
Nkemdilim Caroline Amuta (14)	103
Rhianna Scott (13)	104
Halle Charlotte Yangin (13)	105
Aimee Lines (13)	106
Jasmine Marquez (14)	107
Lowena Harriet Cornish (13)	108
Rose Manser (14)	109
Grace Watson (13)	110
Hayley Wellbelove Kitchen (13)	111

Harris City Academy, Crystal Palace

Annalise Olivia Hallier-Lowe (12)	112
Charlotte Kirby (12)	114
Olivia Addo-Nyako (12)	116
Shaunna Dede-Bamfo (12)	117
Mubarak Mahamoud (11)	118
Asuma Jalloh Jalloh (12)	119
Zack Ejeta (12)	120

Islamia Girls' School, London

Maryam Yussouf (13)	121
Zahra Fautima Styer (15)	122
Jinan Ali (13)	124
Sara Mohammed (14)	125
Mehzanaz Khan (13)	126
Hani Gure (12)	128
Balsam Sadek (13)	130
Shahd Al-Samarrai (12)	132
Hiba Bassou (15)	134
Amina Nessa (14)	135

Sara Ali (11)	136
Manaal Khan (15)	137
Yasmina Mohamed (14)	138
Safa Alam (14)	139
Laaibah Shaad (14)	140
Safia Raja (13)	141
Zeinab Jeilani (12)	142
Shayma Ahmad (12)	143
Maryam M Abdulrahman (13)	144
Iman Khadijah Kamarul Hadi (14)	145
Jenna Al-Samarrai (14)	146
Maryam Zeeshan (16)	147
Mahveen Hussain (14)	148
Batool Sadek (14)	149
Siddiqah Maria Khan (12)	150
Safiyyah Rahimi (14)	151
Farah Nazef (14)	152
Malaika Kashif (15)	153
Noora Hasan Alamin (14)	154
Ariana Islam (14)	155
Asiya Saqib (12)	156
Hafsah Nasser (15)	157

St George's College Weybridge, Addlestone

Ryan Geraghty (12)	158
Izzy Jesshop (12)	161
Michael James Tibbitts (12)	162
Sienna Wootton (13)	164
Harvey David Smith (12)	166
Joely Kay (12)	167
Elliott Healey (11)	168
William McDougall (12)	169
Ece Tagmac (11)	170
Charlotte Fleming (12)	171
Mathilda Luise Bowen (12)	172
Carter Catterall (11)	173
Lucy Ellen Cowland (12)	174
Gabrielle Geoghegan (11)	175
Lucas Parsonage (11)	176
Riley Morris (12)	177
John Carter (12)	178
Tara Burke (11)	179

Ollie Binns (11)	180
Harvey Doran-Nesbitt (12)	181

The Compton School, Finchley

Tarlan Mohammadi (13)	182
Rebeca Carvatchi (12)	184
Scarlett Joanne Olivia Khan O'Keefe (11)	185
Melisa Shirvani (12)	186
Maryam Ahmed (12)	187
Natalie Chu (16)	188

The Urswick School, Hackney

Jasmine Kisembo Rahera (13)	189
Joe Owen (13)	190
Lucas Narbrough (11)	193
Miriam Hammond (12)	194
Huseyin Kanli (12)	196
Valentina Hernandez Castrillon (13)	198
Alvin Ositelu (12)	200
Esther Summers (12)	202
Noah Penton (14)	204
Jayden Greenaway-White (13)	206
Taejah Barrett (12)	207
Alesha Hoque (13)	208
Jude McCaughren (13)	209
Sudenaz Top (15)	210

THE
POEMS

Being An Autistic Teenager

I am a teenage girl with autism
Everyone likes my sarcasm
Having autism makes me unique
It doesn't mean I'm silly or I can't speak
It doesn't mean either that I am weak
I have poor eye contact and that is a fact
I am sensitive to touch, so don't do it much.
I like to have warning, so I have a plan in my head.
When I get stressed, it makes me depressed.
When I get angry, I need my own space.
When I get my own space, I'll go to my favourite place.
I like a very small space in a large, open place
I think you're mean, if you change the routine.
I don't like noise, especially from boys.
When I hear noise, it makes me feel mad.
Yet when there is no noise, I am very glad.
When people shout, I want to walk away.
If I walk away, please don't stay.
I don't like big crowds,
It makes me feel like I'm stuck in one big cloud.
This is my poem about being an autistic teenager.
It's nothing major and I'm not in danger.

Evie Judges (16)
Broomhill Bank School (West), Tunbridge Wells

A Glitch

A box was there to tick, for my gender, a boy was the pick,
A strong boy, an able boy,
What my parents wanted, what they needed, was a boy.
But as the code was found, and I was made stitch by stitch,
As issue occurred, a mental glitch.

When I was five, my mums laid out what I was meant to be about,
As they both were wounded, and gender equality is a bit messy in 2236,
And as one was blind and the other has a bad leg, and you can be hurt by those in 2236,
I was to be a shining knight, if the world was but dark I would be the light,
But you see, I was just, not quite right...

My parents' deformities were to do with the genetic crisper,
As things like defective limbs and lisps are.
It is very rare, so there is not much support for people who are dealt that you know,
And as human birth is completely customisable with everything from body to mind, well, you know,
Parents will make their children as they need them to be, but
Genes have their own ideas about what you will be,
And so, it was with me

When I was six, training my muscles, a piece of clothing caught my eye - pink with tassels,
I knew from first look I was wrong to like it, but it was beautiful,
It might have been slightly better if I noticed the girl, but the dress was the thing I found beautiful,
I suddenly understood that within me something was wrong,
that if I played my cards wrong, I would not belong,
But for my parents, and for the world, I would have to be strong,

And so, I was for ten more years, my mind always dancing and crowded with fears,
And then I couldn't carry on with it and I had to do something, so I said it,
The love of pink and the finding things beautiful, I said it,
I broke off the chains and the shackles, ready to face the hooting and the hackles,

And now without that fear, I am shivering and standing
A box is there to tick, some of it might make you sick,
But if I want to stand tall, then I must fill mental tests in the cold of the glitch room,
Hope I make the test, hope I leave the glitch room,
For my parents can say, "Sorry, Ben, we'll just have to try again,"
For you see, a physical glitch is one thing, and a mental one is another,
That is the distance between the world, people like me and my mothers.

Joshua Wickers (16)
Broomhill Bank School (West), Tunbridge Wells

The War Of Death

We've been walking in the mud for ages,
We have sores on our feet
And yet the pain is awful
It's so bad that it can be dreadful
The sight of the pale people
Can be so hard as the gas goes in their lungs

"Now boys! Put your gas masks on, now!" he says,
As fast as they can run, they try and put their gas masks on
One person falls behind and stumbles in the sludge
I rush back to get him, but when I reach him, he is dead
He is got, red everywhere
We all had dreaded to lie to our children

The Devil's juice pours from his wounds,
And all my dreams of hope have gone
And the war is almost done
And we never know how long it will last
And yet we'll never know who will die last

The faces on all the boys are devastated,
In which they think they may go
Why? O' why would this happen?
If this happened, why did we do it?
And yet I wish it would already be over

The Devil's juice pouring out of the wounds
It's as red as the red in the fire
Why the fire is hot but not as red as the
Devil's juice

And yet as we see the dead and wounded,
All our hopes and dreams fade
And all our friends that we knew faded and
Disappeared
In the blink of an eye, more and more bombs
And more people get...

Keira McNary (14)
Broomhill Bank School (West), Tunbridge Wells

World War One: Life Inside The Trench

Here I am stuck down in this muddy trench
I can hear the guns blazing overhead
The sound of battle has begun
Bombs dropping out of planes at a fast rate
If it hits you you are done for
There is no second life in this world we live in.
Soon it will be our turn to go over the front
Men dying all around me at a fast rate
Never again will I see the day dawn.
Never again will I see my family or sleep on my bed
Or see World War One come to an end
Never again to see my friends or the heroics of the brave
soldiers facing the battle of life or death
Never again
Never again
As men slowly die in the painful sleep of death
Suffocating into darkness until there is no more life left in
them
Never again.

Halwest Brown
Broomhill Bank School (West), Tunbridge Wells

A Nation Divided

Disenfranchised
Disillusioned
A nation, seething
Filled with frustration, rolling with hatred
Stuck, hopeless/repeated on a loop
Parliament - sceptical, a spectacle
Polarised
Provocative, now inciting violence
Propaganda
Intolerance on the rise
Suppression of speech - fear of politics
Protests/more environmental awareness - but time?
Lies, personas and political games
A distraction - Brexit, Brexit, always Brexit
Knife crime on the rise - ignored
The NHS cracking at the seams under the strain
Lack of integrity, lack of knowledge, lack of trust
A social rat race
Birth, education, employment, death
A country ruled by the uninformed
My country - a nation blindsided.

Rebecca Jane Sheahan (18)
Broomhill Bank School (West), Tunbridge Wells

Cat

Fluffy, furry creature, who is a lovely creature. Sleep on your
bed and maybe your head.
It might be a ferocious, funny feline.
Meowing, hissing feline is a curious, loving feline.
Pink, sniffing nose, jumping up fences, making other cats
jealous, jumping and bumping along the fence.
Hiding in a tiny space, rubbing its face with its whipping,
slipping whiskers to see if it can fit through in the tiny
space?
Then pouncing and bouncing on its back legs,
Yelping happily, licking its back leg. Meowing and howling in
the sunlight.
Eating, then going to sleep at noon after eating its food.

Curling and whirling on the bed, then sleeping to the next
morning
Sleeping until the new day begins.

Amber Ella-Louise Jenner (13)
Broomhill Bank School (West), Tunbridge Wells

Teenager

I play loads of games
Sometimes they are lame
They all seem the same
Sometimes my friends call me a different name
Sometimes on my game, I have good aim
I have tons of fame
Sometimes I will tame a dog in my game
Sometimes it sends me insane
I see fog through the window
When I play my game.

Harrison Cavie (12)
Broomhill Bank School (West), Tunbridge Wells

Teenage Life

This is a teenage life
With lots of fights
Every day at school
I feel cool
When I struggle
My friends try and make me giggle
When I'm sad
I get mad
And that is a teenager's life.

Louise Wright (12)
Broomhill Bank School (West), Tunbridge Wells

Surfing

As the sun falls on the horizon,
A sunset like never before owns the sky.
The surfboard shack is still open,
It's time to be free from the world's lie.

As she dips her sandy feet in the cold sea,
A thin plastic bag cuddles her toes.
The surfboard bounces on the waves,
Splashing the seafoam up her nose.

As the woman heads further out to sea,
A swarm of litter floating in the ocean surrounds her.
The surfboard moves slowly when she rides the waves,
And suddenly, the land becomes a blur.

As the determined human paddles her way back to land,
A load of junk touches her palm.
The waves start to get taller,
But she is now safely back where there is no harm.

As the message gets spread across the world,
A small change from everywhere has started to happen.
The small change makes a big difference,
If we make more changes we can save this young surfer's
passion.

Mollie Joy
Burgate School & Sixth Form Centre, Fordingbridge

Home Alone

There is one thing that you should know about me:
I can't be left alone.
Have you ever had this feeling where you can cope with something
Then it gets boring,
Then you go mad and do something mad?

Well, I have.
It was about a year ago,
But it feels as if it was yesterday,
My story of me and the sofa,

I had just come home from a walk,
When suddenly,
Out of nowhere they left me,
All alone at home,

At first, I chewed my best bone,
It squeaked,
A delightful noise if you ask me,
But after ten minutes,
And you probably won't guess,
What happened next...

After the first ten minutes, I just got bored,
But then it turned into something more,
How dare they leave me alone?

But then I had an idea,
A *bad* idea...

The sofa.
Sitting there as it always did,
Never bothering to wake up and play,
Looking so peaceful,
So *vulnerable*...

I couldn't help it,
It was too good to resist!
I pounced at it
Grabbing at the tough material until it ripped, this was *fun*.

It made a tearing noise,
Nice,
(But not as nice as kibble),
And then I moved onto another patch,
And another,
And another...

Until there were no more patches to tear,
Not even a scrap to shred,
Ahhh,
It was nice while it lasted,
But...

... But then the family came back,
Walked through the door,
Saw what I had done,

Dropped the shopping,
And stared at me,

"Mia! What have you done?"
I ripped up the sofa,
I thought that was pretty clear.
"Bad bulldog!" the eldest daughter (who didn't like dogs at all) screamed,
And that's when I *really* realised what I had done.

I don't know what came over me!
"Well, that teaches us for leaving Mia alone," said Mum,
Uh-huh,
They stared down at me with disappointed looks,
I had done the last resort,
I hung my head in shame,
And stared up at them with
Great
Big
Puppy dog eyes...

And got away with it,

But now you know, never leave a child or puppy home alone,
And kids - don't rip up your sofa.

Neve Robyn Hooper (11)
Burgate School & Sixth Form Centre, Fordingbridge

Mrs Lean

My name is Mrs Lean
I hate my job
Teaching children
In primary school.
Well, at least it is not
A secondary school.

It is Monday,
The *worst* day of the week.
I am on my way to school,
The *dreadful school*,
That I teach at.
When I get caught in a traffic jam on the M3,
I ask myself,
"What is it? Where is it?
How long will it take?"
Because if it takes a long time,
It means I won't have to go to that *dreadful school*,
Any longer.

After three and a half hours of constant
Beeping and rage,
I have gotten to the situation,
A lorry has curved all along the lanes of the M3
After police wardens have moved it off the road,
I carry on with my grim journey.

Libby Wallace (11)
Burgate School & Sixth Form Centre, Fordingbridge

Mr Dinge Is Pressurised!

Children. Not any old children but *those* children.
Those children who stare at you in cafés.
Those children who whisper behind your back
And think that you can't hear them, but you actually can
Kind of children.
That's why I hate children.
All they do is cry, burp, fart, sleep and
Irritate everyone around them
But I need to like them otherwise
She won't like me.

'She' as in the one I dream about every day.
The one I dream about having a hospital bed next to.
The one I dream about liking me.
Her name is Miss Bonbon.
Miss Bonbon is as sweet as she sounds.
But her only flaw is that she loves children.

Other than that, we are a match made in Heaven.
I love everything about her. And I especially love her name.
Gwenivere, or as I like to call her, Gwenny.
Oooh, Gwenny, I love you.

She can be my angel in a white apron.
The one who can wipe the food off my shirt
And clean the drool from my face.
And I know that we will love each other forever.

If she knew I had feelings for her
But she will soon know because
Right now I am slowly rising from my wheelchair
To visit her sweet shop down the road

I walk at the pace of a snail towards her bright-coloured shop
And stop at the angelic sight of her
Her wrinkles by her eyes make a shape of a tree on its side
And her smile is big and beautiful
She is mine, I adore her.
I live for her. I would go into a coma for her.
But I wouldn't die for her because
I love myself way too much for that.

Everyone thinks I'm devilishly handsome
And that's why they stare at me all the time.
So it can't be that hard to make her love me.

But now she is walking towards me and I'm panicking.
I can't breathe and I know it's too late.
As she comes up to me, her face fills with disgust.
It is every grown man's worst nightmare.
I can still feel the wet warmth running down my leg:
I had wet myself.

Indigo-Nancy Sonsin (11)
Burgate School & Sixth Form Centre, Fordingbridge

Arch-Enemy

Today I was going to go shopping for my mum
Who is ill
I left the house at 1:45pm
The sun was shining brightly
And I was in a good mood

My mum asked for bread, apples, milk and crisps
I was in the milk section when I saw my arch-enemy
We both stared with anger into each other's eyes
I tried to stay away from him
But then he came up to me and said
"So, we meet again!"

He said it with an odd smile on his smug face
I said with anger
"Yes, so we do!"
He started saying stuff about what happened
At lunch, when we were in school
"Do you remember that time where you fell over with your
lunch?"
He started laughing
I started getting a bit angry
He was trying to get a reaction out of me
He put his hands on me, I pushed them off
He did it again and again
I pushed him away

"Don't touch me!"
I said with rage
He came up into my face
"What did you say?"
At this point, we were both angry
I was thinking of what I should do
He started antagonising me again

He was going on and on
Suddenly, he swung at me, I blocked it
And pushed it away, but he came back for more
He grabbed me and pushed me to the floor
He was feeling victorious
I was really, really angry
I pushed him in the stomach
And slammed him to the floor
Bam! As he hit the floor
He ran out of the shop, battered and bruised
I paid for the food and went home
I told all of this to my mum and she said
"Don't fight, it will get you into trouble."

Joseph Izzard (11)
Burgate School & Sixth Form Centre, Fordingbridge

Guilt

I heaved myself along the street,
Feeling a bit *bored*.
I thought about this morning,
When I was taken to court,
Again.

I stopped.
Children.
Playing in the snow.
My grumpy mood lightened,
I had an
Idea.

I grunted,
"Stop there, children,
What do you think you're doing
Playing in this icy mess?"
They stopped.
They stared.
Then they carried on.

Then I shouted again,
But a little louder.
"I said stop there, children,
What do you think you're doing,
Playing in this..."
I stamped my foot,
"Snow?"

They stopped.
They stared.
Then a boy called out,
"Go away,
Stranger!"
Then the children carried on.

Then I spoke again,
This time I yelled,
"What do you think you're doing?"
I scowled.
"What gives you the right to play,
To laugh,
To smile,
To have-"
I paused.
I took a breath.
Then I murmured,
"Fun?"

They stopped.
They stared.
Then the nearest girl stood up.
"We are just enjoying our childhoods.
What's so wrong with that?"

I stopped.
I stared.

Then I thought back,
To when I was a child.
When no one wanted to play with me.
That feeling of love I always desired.
I exhaled.
"Sorry,"
I muttered.
Then I walked away.
Feeling my first feeling of
Guilt?

Hannah Louise Glargaard Janes (11)
Burgate School & Sixth Form Centre, Fordingbridge

Framed

I ran. Pounding.
The door pounding.
The Body.
The body was in the blood-tainted water in the bath.

I locked the stained bathroom door.
Wiping blood from my ragged hair, thinking.

Shouting,
Shouting came from the door.
"Police, open up!" they bellowed.
I'd search for an exit.
They think I killed,
I murdered him,
My friend,
They shot me for it.

I'd cover him with a towel,
I'd kick a window open by the cracked and beaten-up sink.
I'd light the place up,
Let them burn,
I'd escape the tomb that he... *they* would burn in,
Then,
Then, I'd escape.
Escape the flames.
I'd never trust the police.

Hugh Ellis (11)
Burgate School & Sixth Form Centre, Fordingbridge

The Woman Next Door

I once lived next to a woman,
She was kind and very caring.
She'd always say hello when we walked by
And often gave us sweets but said, "They're for sharing."
When we walked to school, we'd wave to her in her garden
It was filled with flowers of reds, yellows and more
Her garden was her pride, she simply adored

But those days are going and I'm no longer in my youth
I now serve my country out on the field surrounded by ruth
We fight for what's right and what we love
All we want is to give peace like a dove
Violence isn't right but it's all we can do
We only do it because we want to protect you

But recently in my career, I was blown into the air
Pushed back and injured. Honestly, it's not fair.
Though I must not moan about the past
Luckily, I'm recovering impressively fast
I now lay in a hospital bed, idle and bored
And it seems there's a visitor I have lured
She seems old and frail
Not tanned, but pale
I didn't recognise her for a while
Until she came closer, I remembered the smile
She held my hand as I could not move to hold hers
The memories were old, a bit of a blur

But that woman had known me since the start
Although we moved away and were soon apart
She handed me some sweets and looked at me with a kind face
I smiled back, then looked at the strawberry lace
They were the same a woman had given me in my childhood...
That woman was the one who lived next door in my past neighbourhood.

Imogen Grace Carter (12)
Burgate School & Sixth Form Centre, Fordingbridge

My Next Victim

I strode into my back room,
And locked the door.
I opened my cabinet of pristine knives,
And removed the sharpest one.
It was called *red - 1978*

I sharpened the knife even more,
And a smile infected my unfathomable face.
This time I would not fail,
And this time my victim will feel pain,
Not inflict pain on me.

This time there was no second chance,
And this time, the victim would cower.
This time, the hurt I felt last time,
Would finally be avenged.
Finally, I would prevail against my enemy.

My knife was as sharp as a needle,
My heart as cold as ice.
But somewhere beneath that hatred,
Something stopped.
Something held me back.

Shouldn't I be happy, my hurt would be clear,
And shouldn't I be happy my hurt would be suppressed?
But was it right?

I ignored my heart and continued on,
I had no other choice, nothing else and no one else.

My victim had taken my family,
My home, my fortune.
He has taken my entire life.
He was the reaper, the destroyer of my happiness,
And I would crush his world!

Creak!
The floorboard moaned.
I realised I had been stood the whole time.
I was sure of my decision,
I was going to succeed.

I strode out of my back room,
Sharpened knife in hand.
Grabbed my suit jacket.
Put on my hat and readied myself.
I locked the door behind me.

I locked the door behind me...

Ruby Briggs (11)
Burgate School & Sixth Form Centre, Fordingbridge

Regret

I sat in my cell and cried
I know
A criminal like me
Crying
I'm not as mean as I make out
I know that
But I still believe that I did it
I can't believe that I took that dagger in my hand and
No
I can't think about it
And I definitely can't let anyone know that
The leather jacket
The hoop earring
The scowling face
And the cruel eyes
Are just an act

The walls of my cell seem to close in on me
And my handcuffs seem to tighten
And the room seems colder
I shiver
And I can't stop the tears from streaming down my face

I'd been caught with that blood-dripping dagger in my hand
I remember so clearly
The deafening police sirens
The blinding camera flashes

The stench of blood
I knew that my picture would be in black and white
On the front of every newspaper in town

Suddenly
I realise that the door of my cell is opening
Clang! Clunk! Creak!
I'd been so lost in terrible
Terrible
Memories from last year
Still as clear as if they'd been burned into my skull
I wipe my eyes the best I can with chained hands
"Dusty in here, isn't it?" I mumble

A feeble excuse

I allow the young officer to lead me to my breakfast
As I prepare for yet another long day of aching
Torturing
Painful
Regret.

Bunty Buttercup Woodley (11)
Burgate School & Sixth Form Centre, Fordingbridge

Lilly Smith

It was Saturday afternoon,
My stupid parents made me,
Go shopping!
Who even likes shopping?

We went into many shops,
But one.
Mum wanted to go to Flannel,
A very sophisticated, stylish,
Designer shop.

A while had passed,
I was bored,
Very bored.

I suddenly had a sneaky feeling,
Run down my spine...
My hands wanted to rub viciously,
Against each other...
And my mouth,
Wanted to cackle out the loudest,
Evilest laugh...

I spotted something,
Something expensive and shiny,
My arm slowly repelled against me,
Snatching the priceless Flannel bag.
I cautiously placed it around my neck,

As if it had looked like,
Mine!
All along.

Hiding it from my dumb, clueless parents,
We dawdled out of the shop,
But
As we were exiting,
A tall, slim security guard with a red cabbage-coloured
tracksuit on,
Noticed it,
I had left the label on show...
"Young lady!" called the guard,
"Have you paid for that Flannel bag?" he lectured,
"What bag?" I replied with,
My face slowly began to scrunch up,
I went a red colour.

I ran,
Quickly...
I threw the shimmering bag in a bin I passed,
As I ran,
As quick as I could,
(Not very quick)
I fled the mall.

Holly Harper (12)
Burgate School & Sixth Form Centre, Fordingbridge

The Biggest Mistake

I made a mistake!
A very big mistake!
That has changed my life for five years!
And that mistake took place two years ago

I am poor and have no money,
So I didn't have much to eat,
But that day, it was my birthday
And I turned sixty years old!

Thoughts ran in my mind
Should I shoplift?
Should I ask for money?
What should I do?
But because it was my birthday,
I thought I would do something
I had never done before
I was going to shoplift!
As the day came to an end
I thought I could
Go shoplifting late at night,
So I did

As I tiptoed into the shop,
I wondered
Should I do this?
Is this a bad idea?
Should I turn back?

But it was my birthday
I should treat myself
Come on, it's my birthday!

As I appeared at the cake aisle
I saw the thing I wanted
Chocolate cake!
I grabbed
And ran
Oh no!

Sirens went off!
And everyone ran outside
The shopkeeper was calling the police
What was going to happen?

I dodged people and cars
Into a small alleyway
Suddenly
I heard sirens going off
From police cars
At that moment, a policeman
Jumped behind me and
Arrested me!
And that's how I am here
Writing in prison!

Lydia McClay (11)
Burgate School & Sixth Form Centre, Fordingbridge

Never Too Late

Prison
A soon to be normal day
Trying to find my friend
Tom, taken out of school...
Year 10... for...
Murder!

So I robbed,
To get in with him.
My third day in prison,
However...
Still no sight
Getting up...
I glanced in the mirror.

I saw!
Beady, red, anger-filled eyes
From when they arrested my only friend.
Tattoos all over,
One of them a tally of the weeks without him,
Without Tom.
A face blanketed in scars,
From fights with people

And then I thought
How will I do this? One year
To find Tim

Angrily walking to the front of my
Small, dusty
Uncleaned
Cell
I chanted
With everyone else
"Let us out!"

Bang...
The guards were here
To let us out to the yard

I thought about how to kill!
Nothing coming to mind.

Days,
Months,
Nearly a year
Went by
Not long to find Tom.

One day, I woke up,
To the voice of a guard.
He shoved someone into my cell.

My chance to kill!
About to punch him,
A force stopped me.
It...
It was Tom.

He had been here so long...
Only a year left.
I hugged him.
Tom was confused about why I was here...
I told him everything...

Lucy Cooper (11)
Burgate School & Sixth Form Centre, Fordingbridge

Aggressive Me

I was strolling aggressively
While everyone backed
The shop I was aiming for was up ahead
It was the jewellery shop
My intention was to steal

I arrived, the CCTV stared at me as I came to the door
I entered the shop, everyone backed
My voice was deep and scary
Which may have scared people more
The expensive stuff was behind the counter

I had to somehow get there
Then I had an idea
I threw stones into the back of the shop
Then the shopkeeper left and I took all the glory
I was nervous

There was a bang as I left!
I was terrified. I started to walk faster
And faster until I arrived at my van.
I drove home but then the police arrived!
I was petrified!
Did I escape?

Joshua Thomas (11)
Burgate School & Sixth Form Centre, Fordingbridge

The Zoo

The rhinos were immense
They could break down a fence
That is, if they had any common sense

This zoo stank of poo
It was like standing in a loo
I stood there, there were others too

There were orangutans and apes
Swinging in funny shapes
They looked like they were about to escape

I laughed
Everyone thought I was daft
I turned, my stomach churned
They thought I was stupid

I said to a zookeeper, "Is this cruel?"
No answer
He thought I was a fool trying to be cool

There was a poor panda
Everyone stared
And thought it was banter

There was a rainforest section
For animals that needed protection
As I walked, the parrots talked

I couldn't believe it
You had to pay a fee
To come and look at a tree!

What has this world become
It's like a slum
I read a sign by an orca
Apparently, it had been caught by an explorer

I walked past a bear
It had been captured, but where?
I was the only one who wanted to care

I walked past a rattlesnake
I went closer, that was a mistake
Its tail started to shake

This wasn't right
I wanted to fight
But the zookeeper said
"We're shut!" with a sharp bite.

Connor Ings (11)
Burgate School & Sixth Form Centre, Fordingbridge

How Not To Deal With Grief

When I was a boy,
I loved dogs a lot,
But now I am an old man,
I love them even more.

It was an ordinary day, a regular day.
I woke up only to remember that I was lonely,
Lonely as can be.
The only thing I had to talk to,
Was my old, grey Jack Russell Terrier.
I'd had him for decades.

That day, something was wrong;
He didn't come to greet me,
When I called him in the morning
And he didn't seem himself
On the walk that I gave him.

When we got home, it all grew worse;
He dropped on his side while waddling along.
I scooped him up in my withered arms,
And put him in the car.
I drove him to the vets only to find,
His heartbeat slowing down to a slow *budum... budum.*
The vet told me that it was too late
And that we could not do anything
"No! Please, you have to do something."
I shouted at the confused man whilst I was tearing up.

It was too late.
Now, I just sit at home,
Angrily staring down any trick-or-treaters.
When people walk past my old 1930s' house,
They start walking faster until they are striding past my old living room.
Sometimes, I will lure children in with sweets,
Or fake party invitations and they will never see their family
Ever again.

Thomas Smith (11)
Burgate School & Sixth Form Centre, Fordingbridge

Roast Dinners

There's one thing you should know about me:
I love roast dinner
I love it more than my house,
I love it more than my money,
I even love it more than my wife.

Every two days, I have roast dinner
With all those yummy potatoes
And the scrumptious chicken
Along with those delightful Yorkshire puddings
Complementing the gorgeous stuffing
Sometimes, I have roast dinner for breakfast, lunch and
dinner (like today)
I enjoy having it for a snack too

One time, I was having roast dinner
As I usually do
But there was something different
The potatoes were 0.635 seconds undercooked
How dare they!
Disrespect!
"What's wrong, darling?"
I never replied
Instead, I started breaking
All my wife's china plates
And cups

And cutlery
(Yes, they actually make that)

Bang!
Smash!
"Aaargh!"
I hate stupid roast dinner!
I will never have it again!
It's disgusting!

I slept that night
Feeling absolutely outraged
My wife had cleaned all the china away.

My wife woke me up with a roast dinner
It helps me start the day perfectly
I loooove roast dinners.

Julia Van Leeuwen (11)
Burgate School & Sixth Form Centre, Fordingbridge

Mr Canning

Every day,
At break and lunch
I would sneak down
To the basement

I would read
Sometimes, I pretended
I was part of the book

One day, I snuck down
To the basement as usual
I picked up one of the unwanted books
Then I started to read
I found myself in the book itself

I saw evil
My worst nightmares
The sky was pale
It had no expression
I was trapped!
What was I to do?

I tried to run
Not long after, I realised, I was going nowhere
No words could describe
I was trapped
I had to get out of this awful nightmare
But how to do it?

I needed to escape
My only hope was to climb up the walls

I sat on the floor, crying
I couldn't get out
The walls started to close in on me
Then something bad happened
A door appeared
Something small came out of it
It was my long-lost daughter
I needed to get rid of this book
She was skinny and dirty
I cried out to her, "Please, how do I get back?"
"There is no way," she replied
"When you enter, you never leave"
I fell into a deep, sad sleep.

Maisie Somerset (12)
Burgate School & Sixth Form Centre, Fordingbridge

School Trip

As the creatures board the bus
I flick my dry saliva in their hair
Then trip them
Oh how it makes my heart feel warm to see them fall

"The rules
No singing, talking, moving, laughing
And under no circumstance disturb me
Now, if these rules are followed, I will be full of glee
But if just one of you decides to disturb me
Then me being full of glee is not meant to be
Then you will see how mean I can really be"

Teaching
Is not the job to have
When children are rude, horrid, impolite
And smell like mouldy cheese
When I was a child, I was seen and not heard
Nowadays they are heard but never seen
Wasn't life good back then?

There she goes again
Sicky Susan in the back
Everyone looks at me
"Not again!" I yell
"When I was your age, I cleaned it up myself!"

Oh no, we're here now
"Get off, line up you miserable children
Twenty-six
We are missing one"
I can almost hear that ungrateful thing
Oh well, it's their parents' responsibility
"Now, get back on the bus
We are leaving."

Ava Furnell (11)
Burgate School & Sixth Form Centre, Fordingbridge

It's Not Too Late

How is it that you feel no guilt,
When precious life is left to wilt?

Our hopes and dreams have all been crushed,
While talk of Brexit can't be hushed.

You go on about the good old days,
As if climate change is just a phase.

We are left to find the solution,
While slowly dying of your pollution.

You never made a sacrifice,
Now we're the ones who pay the price.

Here we protest during school,
How could anyone be so cruel?

Hopeless thoughts fill my head,
The future is what young people dread.

The blame has been put on your generation,
Because you felt you had no obligation.

Gaining power from deforestation,
No care in the world for God's creation.

All you care about is money,
Please stop acting like this is funny.

We are left to save this Earth,
Because you never cared for its worth.

Maybe it's just human nature,
But we won't forgive you for your behaviour.

That is unless you help fix this state,
After all, it's not too late.

Eleanor Rain Nielsen (13)
Burgate School & Sixth Form Centre, Fordingbridge

The Angry Man With A Warm Heart

I am known as the angry man.
People stay away and keep their distance.
I like it that way.
Anxious parents think I'll slaughter their children,
But I'm not that kind of person.
I'm not a murderer.
Just a very angry, mean-looking man.

I also love to scare people,
Especially children.
If a young child dared to even catch a glimpse of my beefy
body,
They would run like arrows,
Having their dreams haunted by my snarling face,
And my bared, glowing eyes.

I just love it when people get scared.

A few days later,
I went to take a breath of fresh air down the highway street.
I just thought it would be an ordinary day of scaring people,
Having my daily dose of sweet fear,
But something stopped me.
It hit me like an arrow,
Stopping me like it had some sort of handicap of the heart
on the end of it.
As staring at me with beaming soft eyes,
Was a kitten stuck in a tree.

I stared at it,
My thoughts fighting against each other.
Having my devil side defeated,
I reached out and grabbed it.

Thomas Klemz (11)

Burgate School & Sixth Form Centre, Fordingbridge

Riley

I liked to bully
Only I knew why
The fear in people's eyes
I was the *boss*

I'm not all bad
Mum's died
I get abused
Dad's always drunk
Says I should get used to it.

Dad's proud of me when I
Bully!
I liked that,
Made me feel happy.

This one kid,
Freckled face
Big square glasses
Skinny as a chip.

No one liked him.
Not even the teachers,
That's how much of a teacher's pet he is
I shouted
"My homework!"
No answer, I grunted

He stepped back
Embracing himself for a fist

My fist clenched
I lifted it
Gasps filled the corridor
I stopped
It hit me
Realisation hits hard

I felt nothing better, I was quite sad
I now hate my dad

Now I'm normal-ish, well, I think anyway
I helped Dad, I also have a better life
With a good road ahead
Now I have proper friends, better friends,
We laugh, talk, now we have no fear
Standing in-between us, from having fun.

Katie Delaney (11)
Burgate School & Sixth Form Centre, Fordingbridge

Mrs Hoot's Oh No

When I was a child,
I loved getting the bus,
But now...

£2.70?
Huh
I say 70p

Why are these chairs so... so...
Tattered and old?
Ohhwuh!
They're so, so itchy!

First stop now,
Why now?
We're in the middle of a motorway!
Get off at the bus stop,
Doofus!
Let's go now!
I put my hand on the back of the chair
(To comfort myself)
I feel something sticky,
Something gooey,
It is wet,
Eeew!
Chewing gum,
Fresh chewing gum.
Gross.

Screech!
Not *again*
The bus... why?
Crazy people,
Always wanting to cross the road!

Come on, *come on*
Only five yards till the bus stop
Ding, diiiing
Nooo!
Come on!

I stand up,
Walk downstairs to get off the bus...
Puff... poofff...
Nooo!
Off goes the bus,
With me still on it,
But guess what?
The bus doesn't stop at the bus stop!
Aaargh!

Tilly Phillips (11)
Burgate School & Sixth Form Centre, Fordingbridge

At The Shop

The shop was a lovely place,
Aisles covered in brand-new products,
Money waiting to be taken.

"Oh, how lovely," I thought,
Staring at the shiny things,
"Time to take!"
So I ran to the electronics aisle,
Passing all these products,
"This place is amazing!"
As I reached the aisle,
Nearly there,
And snatched a TV,
"I'll have that!"
So I ran to the end of the aisle
"Oh, how exciting!"
Snatched five phones,
"I'll have that!"
So I ran back to the start of the aisle,
Singing away to myself,
And I grabbed an iPad just for good measure.
"Those dumb people at the counter,
Didn't see a thing!"
But, oh, what was that?
A man on the phone?
Look! Who's he calling?
Time to go...

So I ran to the exit,
Dodged the darn security
And out onto the road.

"Phew, that was close,
But, what's that sound?
What are those lights?
Oh no..."

Finley Horbury (11)
Burgate School & Sixth Form Centre, Fordingbridge

The Kill!

I looked over the horizon,
Saw a deer, took a few steps
Then I stopped

Looked a bit closer with my eagle eyes,
Now I saw a smaller one
Then I stopped

Saw a rock, hid behind it,
Now they were looking at the rock
So I hid

I ran into the long grass,
Looked over to see where they were,
I crept a little closer now

Now my eyes were on the aim,
I got ready to sprint,
The deer was going to be shocked.

I got ready to sprint,
Staring at my prey,
So off I went.

Sprinting to my prey,
My prey spotted me now,
So off they went.

The chase was on now,
Took a few turns,

I was glad I had my tail,
I took out my surprise and
My prey was caught.

Finishing it off,
Soon it was dead,
I took it back to eat.

Making sure there were
No animals around to eat
Up my snack,
I ate it in one big gulp.

Lucy Edwards (11)
Burgate School & Sixth Form Centre, Fordingbridge

Prison

The officer dragged me away

Away from my home
Away from my life
Away from everything I knew

I was taken to the station
Far away from my home
Making me feel lost

The scars on my face helped
The people here acknowledged I wasn't a person to mess with
But inside, I felt as timid as a child on their first day of school

Day by day, the same thing happened over and over
Sat in my cell, feeling all alone
The other man in my cell grunts like a pig
While I sit all alone

Over and over every day

They said I had committed murder and buried the evidence
They said I was a vicious man
But I am not a vicious man
I am lonely and lost

My cell was opening, bolts being unlocked
Clunk! Clunk! Clunk!

We were going to be moved into a maximum-security cell
Because we were a danger to others
We didn't deserve a life anymore...

Abigail Theobald (11)

Burgate School & Sixth Form Centre, Fordingbridge

Hiding

I ventured outside
Stumbling down the dark, gloomy streets of New York City
I wondered if they were watching me
Watching my every move
I could see CCTV cameras
It was as if they were glaring right through me
I ran, but my suspicions followed
As I reached the town centre
The lights gave me a sense of safety

The wind whistled in my ear
Calling me to give up the fight for my freedom
People's voices overwhelmed me
So I ran, ran away from all my feelings
My heart was racing
I started to panic
Sweat was now rolling down my forehead
When it happened...

The red and blue lights looked through my soul
The sirens defeated me
I tried to run
But I was surrounded, like a pack of wolves hunting their
prey
I was caught
My anger raged like the devil's cry
I attempted to break free

It was no hope, it was over
My life would now be changed forever.

Harry Garvey (11)
Burgate School & Sixth Form Centre, Fordingbridge

Calling Out But Not Being Heard

She is answered and respected
She is everything to everyone
She has all the love and attention
She can vote for what she wishes

I am broken and unloved
I am part of the darkest of shadows
I am nothing but air
Air of which you can never see
I can't vote for my wishes

She smiles and skips freely down the street
She is never judged
She has freedom and adventure
She does matter

I am slapped by my love
I am hurt for my mistakes
I eat the leftovers of my broken world
I don't matter

We are both very different inside
We should both have the same value
We are loved and unloved
We are in the right and wrong
We should and can matter.

Alyshia Handley (11)
Burgate School & Sixth Form Centre, Fordingbridge

Cheese

I love cheese,
I always have,
I've eaten it since birth,
But my favourite cheese is Stilton,
The stinkiest cheese on Earth,
It makes my tummy rumble,
It makes my bottom burp,
But one day, Mum said, "No more cheese!"
And I completely went berserk,
"No cheese at dinnertime?" I said
"But what about dessert?"
Mum said to have some fruit instead,
But the thought of that just hurt,
I looked in all the cupboards,
I checked under the stairs,
I even checked my secret stash inside my teddy bears,
The thought of having no more cheese made my young heart sink,
But at least I wouldn't do those farts that really, really stink.

Nyah Morgan (11)
Burgate School & Sixth Form Centre, Fordingbridge

Strangers?

Click, the door opens and I hear voices
Thud, thud, thud, they rush towards me
And meet me at the gate
These strangers are so familiar

Creak, the gate opens wide
I fly off the ground and am held chest to chest with them
These strangers know my name
But I don't know them

Then I feel a bit sick
And realise it is happening
Shshshk, my eyes roll back
And I can barely see
It's clear I have a disability

Yet they continue
These strangers feel so familiar
And close to me

The day flies by
And these strangers don't seem like strangers anymore
They're more like sisters.

Anja Phelps (11)
Burgate School & Sixth Form Centre, Fordingbridge

Hunted

Bursting through the leaves and foliage,
A speeding deer and his family,
Are running from hunters sadly.

They run and run,
Until they stop,
A bullet nearly hits that the man shot.

A bullet through the antler,
"Not the head!" the deer said,
"Hopefully not the head!"

A bullet through the antler,
"Not the head!" the deer said,
"Hopefully not the head!"

At last they are safe,
"A day of sleep for us," the deer said,
But the next morning they were back again.

Bang! Right into its head,
The deer is dead,
Smack on the floor,
Oh dear, oh, deer, no more.

Tom Stacey (11)
Burgate School & Sixth Form Centre, Fordingbridge

Painfully Shy

I walk carefully towards the classroom
Pause by the door
Look back longingly
Sigh and step into...
Chaos
One of the girls sidles up to me
"Hi," she says falsely
The way you would talk to a toddler
It's like they think I don't understand
I open my mouth
No words
"Hi," she repeats, eyebrows raised
I turn red
I don't know what to say
So I just stand there
She walks off, joining a giggling group of girls
I clench my fists
Why?
Why didn't I just talk to her?
I couldn't
I didn't
Why?
They are talking about me now, I can tell.

Elly May
Burgate School & Sixth Form Centre, Fordingbridge

An Ocean Of Plastic

Is that for me
A jellyfish floating in the sea
Or is it a plastic bag in the blue, open sea?
I look and see plastic bags or a jellyfish
It could be
I watch what is being dumped into the sea
I think of what the world could be without plastic
Climate change is happening in the sea
There is one thing happening to me

Plastic everywhere
People try to kill me
What could the world be?
An ocean of plastic for me
In the vast, open sea?
What will the world be like in 150 years?
Will it be full of cheers
Or full of fears?
Will I be alive in 150 years
Or dead simply because of plastic in the sea?

Jack Darren Witt (11)
Burgate School & Sixth Form Centre, Fordingbridge

My Birthday

Today is my birthday
I just can't wait to see what I get,
I asked Mum for a puppy,
I hope she didn't forget.

There are lots of balloons around the house,
And banners everywhere,
They all say, 'Happy birthday, Sam!'
It's nice that they all care.

I open my first present,
It is small and round,
It can't be a puppy 'cause,
It doesn't make a sound.

Then Mum remembers something,
And runs out of the room in a hurry,
A few minutes later, she comes back,
With something brown and furry.

"A puppy!"

Ben Stacey (11)
Burgate School & Sixth Form Centre, Fordingbridge

A Safe Place

Ants are small,
They're always afraid.
They are not all,
Everything is big in their eyes.

They see us as giants,
Even though we're not.
The ants are clients,
For their pregnant queen.

Their homes get destroyed,
Always, they run away.
Giants, they must avoid,
Because they hurt them every day.

They are not defenceless,
Some are weak,
And some are restless,
But shelter they must seek.

Do not toy with them,
As a team, they will make you pay.
They are living things,
Please, please just walk away.

Vincent Carter (11)
Burgate School & Sixth Form Centre, Fordingbridge

The Protest

Hello there, reader, I'm the one that said,
"Women's rights are what we need."
At first, no one cared
And all the money and jobs were taken with greed.

Women joined me in the protest
But all there was, was hate.
We carried on demanding
Then I was chained to a gate.

Men were selfish, rude and proud
And had all of the power.
Women had to stay at home
Cooking and cleaning the shower
Later on, the men gave up
We had equality.
Just remember women's rights
Was because of me.

Freya Hignell (11)
Burgate School & Sixth Form Centre, Fordingbridge

Freedom

It was cold,
I was cold,
For twenty years,
The prison behind me.
Was home.

Not anymore.

They had finally let me out,
I was free,
But did anyone remember,
What I did?
All those years ago?
I could only hope they hadn't,
But what if they did?
What would I do then?
Thoughts of,
Past,
Present,
And future,
Filled my mind.

I told myself,
"They won't remember,
It was twenty years ago,"
Then I took the first step to freedom.

Erynn Rodgers (11)
Burgate School & Sixth Form Centre, Fordingbridge

Animal Kingdom

A nimals are dying
N ow they're crying
I 'm sending this message out
M en poaching out and about
A ll beautiful animals suffering in the wild
L ots of animals are now mild

K ing of the jungle is now roaring loud
I 'm now not proud
N othing can stop them from destruction
G od is calling out to us
D on't destroy, you must
O n this present day, animals are dying
M aybe we could do something about this!

Violet Cottrill (12)
Burgate School & Sixth Form Centre, Fordingbridge

The Plastic Blue Ocean

I was a sad whale
Trapped on my own.
It brought me to tears
All the harmful plastic,
Hurting my insides as I eat more to live.
It brought me to tears
As whales blubber, the seasons get harder and some people
care if the world starts to end.
Many animals dying, nobody caring
Until the animals suffer.
And there are no animals swimming in the clear blue ocean.

Help us fight these dying days!
We need more people
To help us heal
The clear blue ocean.

Shannon Wyatt (11)
Burgate School & Sixth Form Centre, Fordingbridge

Through The Dark

Through the dark is all I see
About this woman's heart filled with glee

This woman was not allowed much luck
Because she always failed and people would shout
"Good luck, Chuck!"

She lived in the year of 1938
And passed away with lots of hate

People hated her 'cause she was black
But she would never show slack

This woman was special, not like others
This woman never gave up, not like others.

Through the dark.

James Stubbs (11)
Burgate School & Sixth Form Centre, Fordingbridge

Death Row

He was walking the longest walk
His chains were scratching and screeching
As he dragged his feet across the cold, marble floor
Death was reaching

His time was running short
He cried for a life he lost long ago
As images of his life flashed by
From when the judge stuck him on death row

As he sat down, he prayed the call would come
For someone would seek and find the truth within the lies
As it was about to happen
Then tears ran down his eyes.

Jack Taylor (11)
Burgate School & Sixth Form Centre, Fordingbridge

Please Make Us Visible

Young people are not invisible,
We don't get as much freedom as you do,
Please make us visible.

We have our own rights,
We have our own opinions,
Please, make us visible.

These barriers are making us miserable,
You are the only ones who can unlock these walls,
Please make us visible.

Let the children make the most of their lives,
You can make a difference if you try,
Please make us visible.

Jessica Clarke (11)
Burgate School & Sixth Form Centre, Fordingbridge

Life On The Street

People look and people stare
As he sleeps
He's always there.

People walking in pairs
He lies there watching
And nobody cares.

Starving hungry, it's not fair
I'm well-fed
And yet, he's always there.

If only people learnt to share
Tried to help
But nobody cares

I need to make people aware
He lies there sleeping
And nobody cares
He's always there.

Kitty Davies Bateman (11)
Burgate School & Sixth Form Centre, Fordingbridge

Raiding The Rainforest

It was peaceful there
The way we were all friendly
The way we organised things
It was lovely and peaceful at home

But one day, that all changed
Weird creatures were taking our home away
We were being forced away
It was making us all angry and sad

We couldn't believe our eyes
We had to do something
We made a plan, we were ready to strike
We were ready to take back our home.

Harvey Christian Brown (11)
Burgate School & Sixth Form Centre, Fordingbridge

The Dreadful Place

He was strong
But he thought it was
Wrong to disobey his elders

But soon, the elders
Would make him work ever so hard
He was tired, he was angry

That night, he left without a trace
He was happy, he was
Away from that dreadful place

He would embrace
His dreams
A wonderful time

He would never go
Back to that
Dreadful place.

Drew Merryweather (11)
Burgate School & Sixth Form Centre, Fordingbridge

Different

As I walk down the street
I can feel the heat
Of stares, of glares, of judgmental looks
As my body burns and cooks

I hold my head down
As I walk through town
People laugh, people chuckle
I just hold my head down as I shuffle

"You are weird," they say
"Just go away."
Inside, I am mad
But to them, I am just sad.

Hattie Sims (11)
Burgate School & Sixth Form Centre, Fordingbridge

Believe, Strive, Achieve

Walking on, full of doubt
Fear growing like a vine
Thinking of walking out
I was running out of time

I was going to the line
I thought about tapping-out
I was sprinting for the finish
Fearing I was going to perish

But there I was, across the line
I was feeling so divine
Happiness growing like a vine
A gold medal was mine.

Callum Merryweather (11)
Burgate School & Sixth Form Centre, Fordingbridge

Hopeless

Ah, phew, out of school
Finally home at last
Free from bullies
No running fast

As I check my phone
As I don't trust it, as I'm going home
Texts and notifications popping up
No longer, I feel alone

Sitting and watching videos
When something catches my eye
Oh no, they found my Instagram
Spam and hate make me cry.

Cameron Angus (11)
Burgate School & Sixth Form Centre, Fordingbridge

Save Amur Tigers

The poachers want me dead
I'm not ready right now
Can't they just let me go to bed?
Can I escape, if so, how?

People are supposed to save me
I'm only young
Three months, I'm a baby
Unlike my mum

I want to live
What do I do?
If someone could save me
Would you?

Finn Collie (11)
Burgate School & Sixth Form Centre, Fordingbridge

Come With Me

I smell the food, the bacon and egg
I wish that was mine
Oh, the time has come - it's nearly nine!
The best time of the day, my walk
To get away from the house of talk
How I love the smells
Especially the cake the old lady sells
But now I'm home
And I've got the whole house to roam.

Hebe Eve Forder (11)
Burgate School & Sixth Form Centre, Fordingbridge

A Sofa's Life

I can't handle the pain
But I know I can't complain
A dog on my head, digging its claws in
Its paws lean on me
If biscuits won't make him leave
The pigeons must
But no
Slowly, the pain intensifies
Because of the warm bottom end
They've come to calm him
What a drama!

Elliot McClay (11)
Burgate School & Sixth Form Centre, Fordingbridge

Youth

Y oung people need to be heard
O ceans with plastic, we are constantly coming third
U nder eighteen, our opinions don't matter
T hese sea animals won't be getting fatter
H orses have great lives, dolphins have bad lives. Plastic can take over the world so let us be heard.

Ana Kate Brook (11)
Burgate School & Sixth Form Centre, Fordingbridge

Emergency, Emergency

Dispatch, do you read?
Somebody needs help
The sirens ring
Ding-a-ding-ding!

I jump in the car
Zooming off
Listening for a beat to drop
Ding-a-ding-a-ding!
The sirens ring

Arriving at the horrible scene
Blood, guts everywhere.

Poppy Nutting (12)
Burgate School & Sixth Form Centre, Fordingbridge

Our Generation

Young people are alive
If you stop us, the world won't thrive
Give us wings and we will fly
Our generations are the ones to stop pollution
Our generation holds the key to a revelation
Stop us now and we might just cry
So are you really just going to let the world fry?

Sonny Baum (12)
Burgate School & Sixth Form Centre, Fordingbridge

Trapped Orca

Is this what life was meant to be?
Closed in
Four walls
I long to live free

People looking
People staring
People glaring
Poor old me
If only I was free

When I go to bed
I lay on a piece of lead
I can't wait to be dead.

Jess Horsburgh (11)
Burgate School & Sixth Form Centre, Fordingbridge

The Red Panda

We red pandas like it up in trees,
We're not attention seekers,
We even try and avoid fleas,
So don't judge us quickly.

Our species are quite a few,
But the zoos help us,
But we don't even get a private loo,
How very, very offensive.

Cameron Boydcamps (11)
Burgate School & Sixth Form Centre, Fordingbridge

Death

D epression grew on all the soldiers,
E very day seemed to get longer and longer,
A nd every life, forgotten!
T he food became rationed and horrendous,
H ealth decreased rapidly!

Max Lloyd (11)

Burgate School & Sixth Form Centre, Fordingbridge

My Hero

He helps me when I'm sad,
He helps me when I feel bad
He loves me ever so much,
Even though he was on a crutch

My hero is my dad

I love my hero, my dad
And he loves me.

Harry Paul Lockyer (11)
Burgate School & Sixth Form Centre, Fordingbridge

Daughter Of Despair

Oh, Death
Sweet, greedy illusion
Buried in the deepest depths of dreams,
Be gentle with me
Innocent child,
Daughter of despair,
Who once cried for the light of hope.

Alessia Pavone (17)
Burgate School & Sixth Form Centre, Fordingbridge

Faith

A life God told us to live without fear
Trust in me children and you are bound to hear
The secrets of love, life and death whispered into your ear
For you'll be safe, secure and know where to go
To live life knowing so you can happily grow
Funny that my mind tells me it's a lie
What good God allows young and innocent children to die?
Knowing too much will kill us all
Just as knowing when death occurs doesn't mean we'll survive
Since preventing it could be the reason you die
Love thy neighbour as yourself
And what happens when you don't love yourself...?
I'm not poor, broke or rich
And the hate I hold wouldn't fill the deepest ditch
Thoughts from the past make me smile
To hold on to true happiness just for a while
Living life according to your mind can be hell
If you hold fear the tyrant who has locked you in a cell
I've pleaded, prayed for the pain to ease
He told me, "There is a way for you're the one holding the keys,"

Life is a ride you can choose to reach the end of
Some may jump off early
Or choose to reach their destination

Dear God, please help the children across the nation
For you're the only one who can save this generation
To those who are struggling, overwhelmed by grief
I pray you find the golden light for life is brief
Keep the lost in your hearts every day
They're no longer suffering
Life's hard and it will always be that way.

Nana Agyeiwaa (14)
Chislehurst School For Girls, Chislehurst

Struggles With Identification

Who am I?
Am I British? Jamaican? Am I truly black?
I never actually belonged and, for that, I never loved myself
I didn't feel like I was worth much
People tried to tell me otherwise
But they don't understand the depths of my pain

Leviticus 18:22, the dictator of my life
It teaches that being gay is wrong
My pastor screams it and my parents agree
On the inside, it makes me feel so small
It's like they're belittling me

People preach about freedom, but kick us out of their
kingdom
I'm already terrified, I don't want to have to hide
My blood runs pink, yellow and blue
My love stretches to everyone, even people without labels
too
As open as things may be
My family's eyes are closed
Every word cuts like a razor
Slitting my arm like paper
The blood I bleed is the blood I hide

The need to scream is deafening: my identity is a struggle
From my sexuality to my skin
I don't want to be the sin God says I am, I want to be my
own king

I lost my faith, but I'm ready to accept
I'm British-Jamaican, black and pansexual
I am me and I can finally see
I've won the battle
But now it's time to win the war.

Nicolette Brown-Mason (13)
Chislehurst School For Girls, Chislehurst

My Inspiration - Isabella Bird

It was 1831, the year where I began
The terrifying Victorian era
My future creeping nearer, nearer

At age six, I confronted my local MP
My confidence shouting, "How dare he!"
My insomnia locked me from wonderful dreams
But what I did later is more than it seems

The years drifted by, Victoria reigned
Women stayed in houses as if they were chained
I, however, furrowed a brow
This is something I wouldn't allow

Why should we stay here? I can't take it anymore!
I have a whole entire world that I need to explore!
So I fled out of Britain, climbing onto my horse
My journey began, I had no remorse

From Australia to China and Korea too
All this time, my popularity grew
America was next as my travels stayed long
I climbed many mountains and sang many songs

'A Lady's Life In The Rocky Mountains' was my most famous
book of all
I exchanged my feelings, thoughts on travels and how the
world made me so small

Returning from sweltering Morocco, the final trip in my time I fell dead in the streets of Scotland as I heard a church bell chime.

Carrie Giannopoulos (13)
Chislehurst School For Girls, Chislehurst

My Hero, My Mum

My inspiration is my mum
For showing the strength and work she had done
When facing a life-threatening time
She always went through with a smile that brightened mine

For being a nurse, a mum, a councillor and a friend
When all you faced was something that can't mend
Ask for support and you'll know it'll go to any length
I am always grateful I can count on your strength
Wear that bright, pure halo
You will forever be my hero

When you were in pain, we helped you cope
When I was sad, you gave me faith and hope
Thank you for the guidance you have shown
For giving me a safe place where I have grown
"Life is precious in every way,"
Those are the words she used to say

I will always be proud to call you my mum
You and what you become
The determination we see
And we all have to agree
Makes you stronger each day
In your very own way

Are you my hero? That's the question
There is no other truest inspiration.

Piper Lauder (13)
Chislehurst School For Girls, Chislehurst

Dear Brother

Although my days are cold without you
I have to accept you are gone
How I cry endlessly every night
Thinking about you is so hard

Sometimes the pain gets too much
And then I do stupid things
Slitting my wrists to feel warmth
To be closer to you or even be with you

For six weeks straight you fought
It was a hard battle and you lost
When you were here everything was easy
Now all I have left are memories

Every time I walk into your room
I go into panic, my heart skips a beat
It's been two years but my pain's still fresh
I hear Mummy's cry every night

I regret all the times that we argued
I'd do anything to be with you for a minute
The world's too cold for angels to fly
Heaven's gained another angel

God works in different ways
You were suffering too much
Although it's hard for Mum, Dad and I
It was better for you.

Nkemdilim Caroline Amuta (14)
Chislehurst School For Girls, Chislehurst

I'll Show You

Darkness engulfs me
The light at the end of the tunnel flickers lifelessly
Time walks slowly
Every second, I sink, drowning in my thoughts and emotions
My eyes put up a fight to stay open
I need pills or maybe a potion
I need something to fight for

Then I'm struck with an epiphany
There's somewhere I'm meant to be
Is it a Milky Way or galaxy?
All I know is that you said you'd be there

You said, on days where I hate being me
On days where I want to disappear forever
I should push through the dark clouds and terrible weather
To find you waiting in the magic shop

Millions of lights surround us
Dancing in the night sky
Between us, we share happiness and trust
Now I have a reason to fight, to try
So show me, I'll show you
So show me, I'll show you
Show you
Show you.

Rhianna Scott (13)
Chislehurst School For Girls, Chislehurst

Scars

Frozen rivers descend beyond my neck
and the heart-wrenching pain I felt has now left

Blinding white scars scattered over my arm
tell me how I am safe and free from harm

The tapestry on my skin tells my life's tragic story
and enables me to find strength to love my own body

Scars and bruises are their own language of pain
you can't see it on paper because it's written in our brains

You mustn't feel belittled because of the wars your body has
had to fight
no matter how dark, your soul will always find the light

The ropes of self-hate that once chained me down
made me feel isolated in my ghost town

When you gaze upon the light, you'll never let it go
it's the recognition that my scars are part of me that
inspires me so.

Halle Charlotte Yangin (13)
Chislehurst School For Girls, Chislehurst

Mum

Been my angel since my day of birth
My favourite superhero on this Earth
Who's been there through my ups and downs
You deserve nothing but a thousand crowns

Who says I've inherited her good looks
And called me smart, taught me to read books
Who encourages me, told me to aim high
Said she will be with me till our last goodbye

Who always teaches me wrong from right
Together, we watch the stars at night
She takes me to exotic, new places
And introduced me to familiar faces

She's my favourite lady in this town
And turns my frowns upside down
Told me to never act dumb
These are reasons why I love my mum.

Aimee Lines (13)
Chislehurst School For Girls, Chislehurst

My Puppy Has My Heart

From the day you came
Into my life
My world changed
In the blink of an eye

The happiness you brought
From the first time
You fell into my arms
Closing your small, round eyes

You brighten up the hallway
And jump from couch to couch
Running on back to us
Where you belong

You mean the world to me
And you can change my mood in an instant
I'm so happy
I can call you mine

I love you very much
And I know you don't understand
But my love for you is eternal
Mi Muñecito lindo!

Jasmine Marquez (14)
Chislehurst School For Girls, Chislehurst

Together

At times nobody was there
She taught me kindness and how to share
She's always been a second sister
And told me I didn't need no mister

Her house is like a second home
Together, our imaginations roam
When I cry, she wipes away my tears
Together, we get over our fears

Been friends for twelve years
And together, we will build our careers
Hand in hand, we'll conquer the world
And together, we will swim.

Lowena Harriet Cornish (13)
Chislehurst School For Girls, Chislehurst

Humans, We're Going Down

Humans causing suffering and pain
Some enough to drive you insane
Ruining our planet more and more by the second
Once called beautiful, all now blackened
Killing ourselves faster and faster
No one can save us now, not even the Master
Blood and bodies spilled thanks to our sins
Cuts and bruises on our skin
Burying our heads in technology
It's too late for an apology
Giving everyone a big frown
Humans, we're going down.

Rose Manser (14)
Chislehurst School For Girls, Chislehurst

A World Of Unknown

My portal to an endless world
Gazing into my own eyes
Searching for their keeper
Seeing an unknown stranger
A blaze of crying flames
Then I'm transported to the other side

The side they all think they know
An explosion of colour
A blast of fun
Exploring places; ecstatic faces
A girl who is fireworks

Coming back to gazing in my reflection
I walk away from the range of perceptions.

Grace Watson (13)
Chislehurst School For Girls, Chislehurst

My Big Family

The people who help me most
My dad, very protective, very crazy
My mum, very soft, very kind
My four aunts, very caring, very funny
My four uncles, very weird, very generous
My five cousins, very close, very stupid
My two nans, very serious, very calm
My two dogs, very fluffy, very cuddly
My grandads, looking down, proud
The people who help me most.

Hayley Wellbelove Kitchen (13)
Chislehurst School For Girls, Chislehurst

An Expression Of An Intense Feeling

She felt alone and unwanted in the world
Those girls
Those five girls who made her feel this way
And all this girl felt is *today is my day*
Today is my day when I'll take my life away

"They're coming for you," they would say
They're hunting you down day by day
But the girl didn't care
As today was the day that she'd take her life away

This is my story and it will never change
It's weighing on me, daunting me almost
As I was teased
My insecurities increased
And came to the moment that this was all a nightmare to
me
But this would all end today
As today is when I'll take my life away

School to me is a prison with insecure twelve-year-olds,
struggling to get away
I'm trapped in a room with kids my age who would rather
kill me
Than stare at the monster on the opposite side of the
classroom
When I get home, it's the worst of all
My parents call me a disgrace

I wish I could go back to where I came from, the adoption centre, and hide
Hide away until the monsters go away
Darkness is crawling all around you, don't you see?
Well, tomorrow, you won't see me as today is the day I'll take my life away

Cutting yourself won't change they say
And hurting yourself won't take the pain away
So please, please don't take your life away.

Annalise Olivia Hallier-Lowe (12)
Harris City Academy, Crystal Palace

In The Trenches

People don't understand what it's like
Brutal bloody battling
Afraid when you go to sleep, afraid when you wake up
Afraid of what? I hear you ask
Well, I can tell you; afraid of being alone
Afraid of being killed, afraid of hurting the ones you love
Afraid forever, afraid forever
But it's all over now

Four years of living on rations
But it's all over now
Four years of staring over no-man's-land
But it's all over now
Four years of pain, sadness and fear
But it's all over now

On the 11th November, those bells rang out
The deep pit that sat
In the bottom of what was left of us opened
But the snowy-white images
Of those poor men that were killed in the trenches
Still follows us wherever we go
Tears fell down many soft cheeks
So many that it could fill an ocean

There were hugs and kisses and more hugs
But the ghosts
Of the poor men that were killed in the trenches

Still haunt us forever
The sound of bullets, the sound of feet sinking into the soft mud
And then silence.

Charlotte Kirby (12)
Harris City Academy, Crystal Palace

Seasons

Snow is falling
The trees are naked
Building a snowman, we'll make it!
Hat and gloves on
Let's play before it's all gone
Drinking hot chocolate and tea!

Blossoms grow up upon
Feed the ducks in the pond
Come on, let's see the Easter rabbit!
Growing some little plants
Doing my sun dance
All this chocolate for me!

The leaves turning brown and red
We make a pile and jump instead
Not much sun but that's the spirit!
It's getting kind of cold
The fun never gets old
Watching programmes on TV!

Shining high in the sky
A beautiful butterfly
Getting into our swimming outfits!
Starfish left on the beach
Have an ice cream each
Now, we are finally free!

Olivia Addo-Nyako (12)
Harris City Academy, Crystal Palace

Betrayed Commitment

Awaken to suffocating heavy smoke
The mortified screams of my people
And brutal bloody death of which I could've stopped
But still the feather lies on me

Watching my comrades fall
The furious yet betrayed faces
Pleading me to do what I couldn't have done
Because still, the feather lies on me

My prevention of this could've saved lives
Their lives
Yet still, the feather lies on me
My purpose is pointless
I feel blood where there's a pain in my chest
Eyes are heavy and begin to rest
My slumber continues to tend
But this time, there's no end.

Shaunna Dede-Bamfo (12)
Harris City Academy, Crystal Palace

117

Fireworks

Boom! Bang! Bing!
Fireworks getting
Shot high into the sky
As children eat
Their yummy pie

Bam! Bing! Bang!
Adults having conversations
As children wave their kites
High into the sky
As babies cry

Boom! Bam! Bing!
Fireworks shoot into the sky
As parents wave goodbye
It's coming to an end
Time to say goodnight.

Mubarak Mahamoud (11)
Harris City Academy, Crystal Palace

Here I Stand

I get sat on
I get leaned on
I get written on
I get eaten on three times a day
But nothing in return
I see everything that happens in the family
When they are happy or sad
In their rights and wrongs
I see everything
And I see anything
And everything I see
I can never unsee it
What am I?

Asuma Jalloh Jalloh (12)
Harris City Academy, Crystal Palace

Bullies

I feel like I'm stuck in the dark
And there will never be light
I thought I was like everybody else
But I guess that's not right
How much more can I take
Without constantly trying to break?
Every day I walk through the doors
My body starts to pause.

Zack Ejeta (12)
Harris City Academy, Crystal Palace

The Boy Up My Road

The pressure burdening you is relentless
Seething and receding like a cruel greeting from the
malicious ocean
They made a promise they couldn't keep
They filled your ears with sweet mockery
You needed drugs but your money was tight
Trusted talks became fuel to your fire
They tormented the truth and deceived you as a liar

You owed money, your time is up
You might as well just give up
The telephone sat melancholy in the dusty hall
No one bothered to call
You eased off drugs, amended your behaviour
You ceased taking your life-threatening paraphernalia

Now you're clean, innocent, pure
You're on your way to the store
The silver metal shines so bright
The foot-long machete glinting in the light
You're asphyxiated, stabbed six times
You take a deep breath, the panic resides
Your time is up, you utter, "Goodbye."

So go to sleep, close your eyes
Dream about your family's goodbyes because
You will never wake up again.

Maryam Yussouf (13)
Islamia Girls' School, London

Not Like Other Girls

Belittled, ignored, objectified
Laughed at, mocked and patronised
You belong to anybody but yourself
And every facet of you is up to be criticised

Whichever way you are
There's no escape from man's critique
They say you're not like other girls
Your pretence makes you unique

Your decisions are all made for you
You hardly get a say
No other path than the one they've set
This road of roses is thorny all the way

Cover yourself in make-up
And when they tell you, you'd better smile
Life is a test and you're in court
But there's no justice in this trial

So put yourself on show
You're no more than an idle display
Either that or your skin is shameful
Kept in the dark and hidden away

Scarred skin is a canvas
To keep under covers or to adorn
Paint it the way the people like
No weapon sharper than man's scorn

But something so pretty cannot belong to you
And if it's taken, only you are to blame
Let them point their fingers and laugh
You were the fool who's to wallow in shame

The second you were a woman in this world
Your entire being became a commodity
Because you can only be a product
When you're sold just by your body.

Zahra Fautima Styer (15)
Islamia Girls' School, London

Truth Serum

Is this the life I used to kick my mother's womb for?
Lies, lies, please, no more!
Apology accepted. Trust denied.
My heart now paralysed.
My feelings spoken to a deaf man,
Alas, I awaited the truth from a mute man.

Trusting someone comes with doubts
Oh, how the truth comes with outs;
A person for life or a lesson for life,
Truth serum cuts like a knife.

What pours from my eyes is a melting soul,
What fractures my heart is a flame
Apology accepted. Trust, I might gain,
Indulging in memory's rapturous pain
Lies, lies, they still remain.

You see the stars
And I see rotting bars
Birds in cages, spending their ages
Because their guilt was beauty
My mind still sooty
Demons of light and angels of fire,
Spit the truth far from my desire
I drink the truth serum,
Awaiting to face the theorem.

Jinan Ali (13)
Islamia Girls' School, London

Truth

I am the petal that flew from its flower
I am the queen, yet I have no power
I flow freely through this world of imagination
And, as wind flows through me, I feel no sensation

I have been lied to countless times before
But that didn't stop me from coming back for more
I am addicted to the lies

But no matter how hard I try
I cannot break free and fly

Sometimes, I wonder
Why me?
But I have soon come to realise
I am not one of the lucky fishes in the sea

The voice inside my head lies
But it won't let me know
I gave up on ignoring it a long time ago

I was the petal that flew from its flower
I still am the petal that flew from its flower
I will always be the petal that flew from its flower
I will never be the queen I aspired to be
Because what's a queen without any power?

Sara Mohammed (14)
Islamia Girls' School, London

Untitled

Blood
All I see is blood
All I see are bodies
Covered in rust and blood myself
Everyone's blood but my own

Bullets firing out of me
Into the bodies and heads of young souls
Young, innocent lads
Yet they did nothing
Just there to fight for their country
For their home

But it isn't my fault
It's 1912, the middle of the war
I see old chaps
Lying on the battlefield
Lifeless
Their souls taken away from their bodies
Stolen
Like priceless pieces of art

A gun
It is what I am
Having to kill by force
It is what I am
Having to kill without choice

I want the bloodshed to stop
But I am anything but a peacemaker
It isn't what I am
Having to be controlled and having to watch the death
Murderer
I am a murderer.

Mehzanaz Khan (13)
Islamia Girls' School, London

The Life Job

I stay paralysed
In a mountain of stone
In the usual position
Following my family's tradition

I see people every day
Pass and go
No one giving me a second look
Consumed by their own book

I feel distressed
Never seeing the same person twice
People coming back; never the case
As I stay rooted in the same place

I hear people bustling around
I see them speak and listen
I have a voice that no one hears
But I hear their loud voices
As they speak into my delicate ears

I am a lion statue
Outside of the Queen's Palace
I have no satisfaction
As I am a tourist attraction

I do not get any peace
Twenty-four-seven I stand
I have one more unfortunate message to send

There are no words left to rhyme
This is the very end.

Hani Gure (12)
Islamia Girls' School, London

Trust

A secret
A lie
A hope
A trust

Some secrets are told
Some, you hold
Some secrets you don't want to remember

A lie that you say
Can always make you pay
No matter the situation
You'll never find a way

A hope can be exciting
A hope can be sad
A hope can be lovely
But may make you mad
A hope can be evil
Which can also be regretting
But, nevertheless, will always portray your image

Despite all of this
A trust is a must
No matter what you do, it should always come first
Trust is like a glass
Once smashed, it can never be the same again

The things you do
The things you say
It is always the image
That you portray
All the pain
Will go like rain
But will never be forgotten again.

Balsam Sadek (13)
Islamia Girls' School, London

Homeless Child - Mother's Return

I sat on the street side
Mother said she'd be two minutes
I'm hungry, quiet and refuse to talk
I hold up my sign
Hoping the nice boys'll come

It's been a while
A month or so
Mother said two minutes
No sight of her
I've begun to lose hope

The nice boys are mean
They stole my money
And said things I'll never repeat
My eyes look fuzzy
It hurts

I'm now alone
They're all gone
I'm searching for food
People always stare
Now I'm going to move
Walking and walking

I see these kids with mums and dads
But they just moan and groan

They're really ungrateful
I wish I was there

It's been a while
Mother's not back
Not now, not ever.

Shahd Al-Samarrai (12)
Islamia Girls' School, London

Hope

I am a wanderer
I wander through the hearts of those
filled with shouts, screams and cries of woe

I lift the spirits of broken souls
witnesses of the world's darkened holes

I am the cause of the most purest of smiles
and the drive to walk a thousand more miles

I am the key to mending destruction
the guide I am with the set of instructions

I am a traveller

I travel through crushed nights
bringing forward the lost pure light

I crawl through the most blackened of minds
thinkers of fear, pain and self-demise

I am the bird that perches in your chest
flutters its wings, putting your worries at rest

I am the hand that wipes away tears
easing hardships, diminishing fears.

I am Hope.

Hiba Bassou (15)
Islamia Girls' School, London

King's Slave

The ether alight with storm and flame
An endless ringing of a senseless vow
A hollow heart bound with cuff and chain
Bore the weight of a paper crown

Evading his shadow cast over the sky
Blinding myself to the havoc he would bring
As I pondered how such a bitter lie
Could've made such a bitter king

My sword ready between my fingers
As the king plunged deep into my eyes
No hope remained to linger
No longer could I believe my lies

I flew to the castle window
And looked hesitantly at the kingdom ahead
I once again wore my robe
And fixed my crown atop my head

Bodies laid prettily on the floor
I was a man with a broken chalice
A lone soldier in a lonely war
A man with a broken palace.

Amina Nessa (14)
Islamia Girls' School, London

Truth

I am the truth, not a traitor, but the truth
What has this world come to?
All falsehoods stuck in boots
Looks may deceive, like a bee, up in a tree
But really, they aren't that bad
Like others may be

Sometimes, I begin to ponder
With my head up in the clouds
I think of being an angel
Living sweet and sound
But, back down, living on the Earth
It's not like that right now
Maybe that can change
If I don't get into a row

I wish this world was peaceful
Full of truth and full of gold
And it could be me who made that happen
If I spoke up and didn't hold

This world could be divine
If it was full of truth
Then it wouldn't be you
Who had lies stuck in their boots.

Sara Ali (11)
Islamia Girls' School, London

Strong

They say never give up
Never give in
Keep fighting that fight
So the Devil doesn't win
Through the hurt and the pain
Through the sorrow and the shame
The one thing you need to remember
Is tomorrow is never the same

Hold onto your hopes and dreams
For your fears are less than they seem
So to all those who feel like they are losing a fight
And to those who feel like there's no hope in sight
Take a minute to look at the sky
And remember that there's something out there
Bigger than you and I

Just like today
The sun will shine again
Through the clouds and the rain
The sun still remains
And eventually, all the darkness will fade away.

Manaal Khan (15)
Islamia Girls' School, London

Here For You

Every day
I'm stuck with you every day
Hearing everything you say
Gossiping and lying
Using me as your mouthpiece
When does the truth come in?

It comes in when you're sat alone
Thoughts to yourself
Concentrating
Not when you're spreading rumours
Ruining people's lives
We're all in one hive
We should be comforting one another
There for each other

The truth is there is no truth
It's always altered
If you haven't figured it out yet
I'm your phone

I'm here for you when you're all alone
I know the real you
No lies
I know who you are, beyond skin deep.

Yasmina Mohamed (14)
Islamia Girls' School, London

138

The Truth About China Camps

It's dark in here,
I can't see,
Maybe it's because,
There's a blindfold on me.

I'm chained in here,
My hand bleeds,
They took my family,
They, the Chinese.

What did I do wrong?
Where did I sin?
Or is it because,
I'm a Muslim?

I'm not on the news,
Nor do the government care,
The real truth is,
You won't see me anywhere.

They're harvesting organs,
I hear the screams,
I can only imagine,
The horrible scenes.

I think I am next,
They're sharpening the knife,
Well I guess it's time,
See you in the afterlife.

Safa Alam (14)
Islamia Girls' School, London

The Wolf

I run wild, I'm untameable
That's what you see
I'm strong and uncontrollable
You can't save me

But inside, I'm someone different
You don't try to see
I'm gentle and protective
You don't know me

Fighting for survival,
You see me a predator
Saving my family
From my mortal enemy

My soul, my heart
Different yet not apart
I'll kill you if you dare
So stay away, beware

I'm here whether you see me or not
Come near them and I'll watch you rot
Don't you dare, I'll trust my instincts
I am a wolf, I'll trust my instinct.

Laaibah Shaad (14)
Islamia Girls' School, London

I Am Only Human Is The Truth

This is the truth
I have betrayed you
This is the truth
I have lied to you
This is the truth
I don't feel sorry
This is the truth
I will do it again

This struggle goes on and never ends
The truth will come out
Wherever I turn, I see it
The truth

Absolute truth is what I say
People are my expectations
And in reality, I am all alone
It is everything but the truth
What I see, feel and talk about is everything but the truth

But doesn't everyone make mistakes?
The truth is that I lie
The truth is that I am only human
And that
I will make mistakes.

Safia Raja (13)
Islamia Girls' School, London

Truth

The truth is something very rare
But really should be used everywhere
The truth is golden but so is silence
So, if you don't have anything useful to say
Don't say anything

This is the truth behind reality
This is what many of us face
I am a Palestinian girl
Locked up behind bars

My dad was killed before my eyes
And my mother and brother ripped away from my hands
My family were innocent
As innocent as can be
They never wronged a single soul

Now, here I stand today
Speaking out for the voiceless
Speaking out for the oppressed
And I hope something is changed.

Zeinab Jeilani (12)
Islamia Girls' School, London

Truth Behind The Bars

Preaching for the truth is what got me here
In prison, behind bars
Cowering in fear
Trying to hold my head high
Failing after numerous tries

Getting served the same poisonous food
In prison, behind bars
Their faces gleeful and crude
Trying not to tremble
Failing after numerous tries

Receiving whip and lashes
In prison, behind bars
Patterned bruises after the bashes
Trying not to cry
Failing after numerous tries

Staring bored at the wall
In prison, behind bars
Impatience in my every yearn and call
Trying not to give in
Failing after numerous tries.

Shayma Ahmad (12)
Islamia Girls' School, London

Famous

On the screen
Hair done up
Looking perfect
Smiling with our pearly teeth
We are famous

People believe we aren't depressed
We have great lives
Nothing less
We start trends
And make them end
We are famous

We have shiny eyes
Perfect smiles
Happy hearts
Lots of money
Supportive fans
We are famous

But little do they know
Those smiles are plastered on our faces
Those hearts are broken with pieces all over the place
The money we have gave us debts
Those fans who support us don't know our real selves
After all
We are famous.

Maryam M Abdulrahman (13)
Islamia Girls' School, London

Miracles Of A Star

"I don't see anything," said the boy
And the old man smiled,
"Look closer, tell me what you see."

As I looked up once more,
A twinkle of light sparkled in the night sky
Then another and another
Soon, the darkness of dust was nothing
But a background of stars burning

I saw the joys of life
I saw sunsets of pink and purple
I saw fairy-tale dreams
I saw everything that felt like miracles

And, as the night fell peacefully
The stars lit up his eyes
Just a glimmer of hope in his soul.

Iman Khadijah Kamarul Hadi (14)
Islamia Girls' School, London

Freedom

Blue
All my life, I see blue
Everything here is full of life
The reef, the fish, even the little plankton
That's what it seems

Black
The ocean was blue
Now it's black
Oil spill, dead coral, lifeless fish
Everything isn't what it seems

Plastic
At least that's what I think they call it
It's everywhere, my shell, my fin, my head
I'm struggling to breathe
I reach the shore
There isn't any air
I close my eyes
Taking my final breath
As a turtle filled with freedom.

Jenna Al-Samarrai (14)
Islamia Girls' School, London

Until I Rise

My face glistens with moist tears
Eyes red and cold
The mirror reflects my skin and bones
But most of all
My broken soul

I trudge along the stony pathways
Eating scraps
I need to survive
Hair matted with the rain
Wondering where I will sleep tonight

Hands clench, heart pounds
At the thought of my home
A vivid memory
From long ago

Broken I am
But I'm sure I will rise
From the depths of the streets
To the horizon and beyond
It's only a matter of time
Until I rise...

Maryam Zeeshan (16)
Islamia Girls' School, London

Truth

Speak the truth, it's the right thing to do
Telling lies will haunt you through and through
How will you be able to sleep at night
Knowing you hid the truth from plain sight?
Will your conscience ever be clear?
Why would you want to live in fear?
How many lies would you have to tell
To keep the truth hidden, it may become hell
Keeping quiet is not always correct
Stand up, shout out, withstand, object
Don't be shy, be brave, be bold
The truth will come out, it shall be told.

Mahveen Hussain (14)
Islamia Girls' School, London

Captured

Freedom! I have freedom to soar through the sky
I watch my friends fly above the mountains
But are we really free from the grasp of humanity?
Locked up, bars and metal surrounding my freedom
I deserve to fly through the heavens of the Earth
I am a bird
Don't I deserve my freedom?

Of course I do, what makes me any different to the rest
Of the creatures on this Earth?
All I wish is to break free
Break free from the chains of humanity
I am a bird and I deserve my rights!

Batool Sadek (14)
Islamia Girls' School, London

We're Not How We Seem

We are young and we don't listen to you
We will grow into something else
We cry when we're blue
We still need you, no one else

You're fed up of us
We cause such a fuss
You always care
And are always fair

Don't go away
Without you, we're astray
You always make me smile
And always make me grey

But most importantly, we love each other
And we'll be together forever and ever.

Siddiqah Maria Khan (12)
Islamia Girls' School, London

Adrift

I'm sinking into the ground
Each step I take leads me further and further into a deep,
dark hole
A trap
Day by day, I watch my friends vanish into the sinkhole of
the earth
The greatest threat to my kind
The ocean
As the sun overpowers the icy kingdom that once existed
I wonder
Will my mystical land still lie here tomorrow?
Or will my homeland deteriorate before my eyes?
I am a polar bear
Will you help me?

Safiyyah Rahimi (14)
Islamia Girls' School, London

Chaos

Walking, walking
Blood on the ground
Gunshot here, gunshot there
Person in the corner
Dead

Walking faster now
This is not my fault
Tank here, tank there
Turn a corner, phew
Here's my mother
Dead

It's been happening
For more than a decade now
But nobody cares
Ignorance here, ignorance there
They've found me - *Bang!*
Here I am
Dead.

Farah Nazef (14)
Islamia Girls' School, London

Often

I feel like no one understands me
And everything a teen has to go through
I feel as if I will always be alone
And the sad thing is no one ever asks
"How are you?"
So we pretend to put a smile on
And behind it, is many many tears
Maybe that's a bad thing
A person full of smiles
That's who I am now
But I like it like that
But inside, you'll never know.

Malaika Kashif (15)
Islamia Girls' School, London

My Painful Life

I look above
I see murderers
I see big feet
I see my friends dying
I feel my heart breaking
All I can do is run to them
But then I realise it's too late
They're gone
Forever

I can't stand up for our rights
Because I am a little creature walking peacefully on
the floor
I am sad, I am heartbroken
But I can't do anything, they are humans.

Noora Hasan Alamin (14)
Islamia Girls' School, London

Bullying

Danger, when they look into my eye
They don't understand
They make me want to die
Don't look at it
They call me an 'it'
Why put me in this pain?
Instead dump me in a pit

Terrorist, what does it really mean?
It is heart-breaking
To know this is how I'm seen
Never make the mistake
Don't judge a book by its cover.

Ariana Islam (14)
Islamia Girls' School, London

Hope

Is there any hope?
In these darkened times
All help is lost
No words are left to rhyme

Crouched in the corner
Tears run down my cheeks
I stare down at my hand
Does my colour really matter?

Like you, I have hopes and dreams
So why destroy my future?
Just because of something in my genes
My thoughts matter just as much as yours.

Asiya Saqib (12)
Islamia Girls' School, London

From A Teenager's Point Of View

Sometimes I wander
Wander through my thoughts
And as I ponder
I am at a loss

The words that I hear
Are no different from what I think
But as I near
My heart starts to sink

I stare at the floor
Questioning my existence
How was it before
Before my persistence?

Hafsah Nasser (15)
Islamia Girls' School, London

In The Rainforest

Slithering through the rainforest, without making a sound
While the chaos of the rainforest happens all around
As I slither through the undergrowth, looking for my prey
The trees loom overhead, blocking the light of day

Screeching aloud, the macaws fly overhead
As I look up, I see their vivid shades of red
A poison dart frog is sitting on a leaf
I look at his colours in disbelief

I come to a river, I fancy a swim
But the water looks murky and a little bit grim
I see a caiman on the opposite shore
That's strange, I've never seen him before

I'd better get moving, start heading back
If I get too near, things will end up black
I head back to the safety on the trees
Now all I hear are the monkeys

An orangutan with his great orange hair
Seems to have been given a scare
Oh no, a green anaconda is getting near
Should get moving, I shouldn't be here

I manage to get away from the other snake
I can't get reckless, raising the stakes
I'm getting hungry, I need food
I need to eat or I'll be in a bad mood

The noise of the river fills my ears
While the rainforest isn't as it always appears
Goliath Birdeaters lurk in the dark
And piranhas ready to pounce like a shark

As I make my way through the trees
I start to feel a gentle breeze
I spot my target, I make it my prey
I will make certain this will be their last day

I creep slowly closer, reeling them in
Getting ready to put them within
I get into position, ready to strike
Then I start thinking we're really alike

Fighting to live, fighting to survive
Just being grateful that we are still alive
It's survival of the fittest, that's what I thought then
I am the fox, they are the hen

I whip my tail, coil it around
Until they are unable to mutter a sound
I gradually squeeze tighter each breath
There is only one ending: certain death

Once my prey is dead, I swallow them whole
Very glad my stomach is under control
Now I'll go and relax up a tree, off the floor
As I won't need to eat for weeks or more

I will just find a place to hide and chill
Have some time out before my next kill
Somewhere out of the way of lurking threats
And go to sleep where one forgets.

Ryan Geraghty (12)
St George's College Weybridge, Addlestone

Teen Relationships

My phone goes off, a little beep in my coat
'We're done, you player,' that's what my boyfriend wrote
I try to cover up my feelings and not feel like a disgrace
But I just feel a tear running down my face

I sit in my lesson, just waiting for it to be the end
I still wish we could just be friends
Looking at the message he sent me again
I reply to it saying, 'What?' and 'When?'

Thinking back about all the memories we had
To be honest, it just makes me feel sad
The boy I sat next to in this class
Said something that smashed my heart of glass

I picked up the pieces and left the room
He shouted after me, I was just wondering who
He'd asked me who I had cheated with
I can't believe people believe this myth

I loved him and I thought he loved me as well
Fired up and so angry, I wanted to yell
But instead, I just began to think
Why are relationships a thing if most of them just sink?

But then I think about the day
That I will meet my forever bae
Some time into the future it may be
However, it will happen to you and me.

Izzy Jesshop (12)
St George's College Weybridge, Addlestone

Tough Time To Be A Leader

Sirens ring loud and far
As I light my cigar
Bright red streaks of death reek around every corner
As the family thinks, *I should have warned her*
Puddles of blood trickle between the cracked cobblestone
As the lifeless body releases a stench of unknown
I look through my window to see rubble and abandonment
All I hear is the distressing sound of torment
Postmen have bags of letters every day
All creating the feeling of dismay
The massacre has just begun
People's lives taken by the gun
When I enter the war room, all is bitter silence
Everyone has a sense of doubt and heartfelt defiance
The decisions are loud
And the bombs are proud
Germans think they're clever
And have a strong endeavour
They would kill everyone, whoever
But they don't know that they will change the face of Britain
forever
The bombs drop
People's lives go pop
And vanish in a bright yellow burst of colour
Which sends their family into sadness over their mother

Concentration camps are like fate
They cause death which isn't great
Jews hide
Most died
And the rest are scared for life
But lots left just mourned their wife
Gas is a killer
On your spine it is a chiller
The bombs are non-stop
And Hitler won't give up
But I pray that all will be for God's glory
I am Winston Churchill and this is my story.

Michael James Tibbitts (12)
St George's College Weybridge, Addlestone

Social Media

Twitter, Instagram and Snapchat too
Are all those social media pages when kids say
'Oh wow, look at you'

Slide in my DMs or snap me back
After hearing about the recent scandal
Mate, cut me some slack

Look at that stunning brunette
Or that man's perfect wife
How bad can it get?

We choose the things we want to show
We all have those things
We want no one to know

Lots of stuff goes on behind the scenes
Much of it shouting
Or watching our screens

Some of the stuff we don't want to display
A thousand awful selfies
A bad fashion day

We are all guilty of comparing what we're shown
Their life 'looks' amazing
"Why not me?" we may moan

But remember there's always another side to the story
People fighting and swearing
Or somebody crying and wrestling with worry

No one has it perfect, whatever we post
We can all feel lonely
Or anxious and lost

It may be that someone looks happier or leaner
However, never forget
Their grass is not always greener.

Sienna Wootton (13)
St George's College Weybridge, Addlestone

The Orphanage

I look out the window with my tear-stained face
And I wonder if there is such thing as God's grace
How could God be so forgiving
If my parents are no longer living?

Rain pours down, I start to cry
As umbrellas go up, facing to the sky
Most boys enjoy it when they're seven
But it's hard to enjoy it when your parents are in Heaven

The building I stand in, a prison of pain
Not least when you're being smacked with the cane
But nothing compares with the pain inside
With all the thoughts of suicide

With all the wishes and all the dreams
And all of life's awful schemes
And thoughts of what life could be
All found inside an orphan like me

I wish I had a mum and I wish I had a dad
I wish I could cry with them when I was sad
I wish I could tell someone that life's not fair
But when there's no one there, there's no one there.

Harvey David Smith (12)
St George's College Weybridge, Addlestone

Life As A Pet

Being a pet dog is the worst
I want to be in the wild where I belong
But I just sit here all day long
Wondering about life outside my home

I would be part of a pack
And would never be left alone
So, I would have unlimited amount of bones
While barking and talking with my real family

The worst part of living with humans
Is they don't know how to speak properly
They talk to me like they have just won the lottery
Speaking like I have no clue what they are saying

Sometimes, I wish I could tell the humans how I feel
My baths are not hot enough
The brush is too rough
But no dog must ever speak to a human

Although I want to go to the wild
I could never leave my human family
That would be a felony
A dog is a man's best friend

Maybe the wild isn't for me after all.

Joely Kay (12)
St George's College Weybridge, Addlestone

A Teenager's Mind

Being a teen is hard, we all know it
But how we deal with it is important
Parents try to do their bit
Everything going through their minds
It's a maze
And they all go through so much pain
Pressure, tears, anger, heartache, hurt... it's hard
Schoolwork, family, friends, bad drugs
Confusion! Are we happy?
Are we sad?
Do we really know?
It's how we deal with it isn't it?
So they all say
Stay away from drugs
Staying away from friends
Do we stay away from everything?
Do we stay away from life?
Pressure with exams
Trials for a sport
The need to succeed
We are only children
But this is real life
It happens to the best of us
We're only human after all.

Elliott Healey (11)
St George's College Weybridge, Addlestone

The Champion

All the runners are waiting at the starting line
Several mouth silent prayers while looking up to the sky
The favourite is in lane four
After what seems like hours but is only seconds, the runners
take their marks
Hearts beating, adrenaline pumping, muscles twitching
The stadium is silent
The spectators hold their breath
Bang!
As quick as lightning, the sprint begins
This is no time to be slow
The crowd stands and cheers, "Go! Go! Go!"
The favourite breaks away from the pack
Tearing down the track to victory
He crosses the finish line without breaking a sweat
Another world record has been set
His champion time is now the one to beat
But that is for another day.

William McDougall (12)
St George's College Weybridge, Addlestone

Prison

Some of us are here for nothing
Captured in tears and screams
For example, like my story
A man shot dead
My stomach was empty
My head in pain
There were screams in my ear
Since then, I can only see but not hear
Blood is now my fear
The man runs away pointing the gun to my head
I was left alone
I saw a police car coming towards me
There I was, a prisoner
Don't look at us like that
Sometimes it's not our fault
But what I wouldn't do
To see the world again
Leave those prison walls
Leaving behind the tall, strong men
The ones that look at you like it's your end
But what I wouldn't do
To see my family again.

Ece Tagmac (11)
St George's College Weybridge, Addlestone

One In A Million

I always stand there, trying to be proud
But then I realise I'm the only one in the crowd
I feel like I'm on a never-ending train
But all the while, I still feel the pain
"You're just unique," that's what everyone says
But still, I feel like no one cares
In my dream world, everyone's kind
But then again, that's just in my mind
They don't say anything but still, it's there
That awkward tension in the air
I always wonder in my bed
What do they think of me inside their head?
My confidence always shatters
But I know that I am one in a million
And that's all that matters.

Charlotte Fleming (12)
St George's College Weybridge, Addlestone

The Chambers

Why him?
He has a family
Waiting for him to come home
Praying he'll be okay

Why not me?
There is no one for me back home
No family
Nobody sitting in a corner, worrying about me

Gut-wrenching screams all through the night
The cries of children being peeled away from their parents
Stuck to them like limpets
Flailing their scrawny limbs around

They drag him down to the chambers
The gravel grating beneath his bare feet
He's screaming but no one can hear him
And then, he was gone
I never saw him again
He may be dead but his spirit lives on
He is remembered.

Mathilda Luise Bowen (12)
St George's College Weybridge, Addlestone

The Tesseract

It's hard for them being squashed
In their flatland view
They think they're right
Limited to their own angle

Scurrying around their flat world

They don't know we exist
They deny we exist
They can't experience us

Scurrying around their flat world

But we can be big and bright like a precious gem
Imagine seeing inside your friends, a bit awkward
Big or small, big and small
4D, 5D, 11D

Perhaps I am just hidden by perspective?

But if you scurry through your flat life
Denying that I exist
Then I wonder sometimes, do I really matter?

Carter Catterall (11)
St George's College Weybridge, Addlestone

Global Warming

Our world is changing
But is it for the best?
The temperatures are rising
But none of us seem stressed

We should be taking action
But instead, we sit in vain
Soon, it will be too late
And then we will complain

I see the climate changing
Nor working as it should
I know this won't be easy
I know this isn't good

I know the cause of global warming
I know the solution too
But the world won't listen to one girl
There's nothing I can do

Unless we all join together
And fix this problem for the better.

Lucy Ellen Cowland (12)
St George's College Weybridge, Addlestone

Trapped...

Sad, depressed, angry, loved, hated, frustrated
This is how he felt
All these emotions flooded through him
Like a tsunami invading his mind
How could he live like this?
Was this how his life was going to be?
His body felt hollow with loneliness
He was trapped in his own mind
Paralysed with fear, he was shaking
Chains wrapped over him and weighed him down
Holding him tight in their skeletal hands
And sucked the life out of him
His mind was a roller coaster of emotions
And was really taking over his body.

Gabrielle Geoghegan (11)
St George's College Weybridge, Addlestone

The Race

I take position
Ready on the starting block
Adrenaline pumps
My heart thumps
I hear the starting gun
I start to run
My legs know what to do
This is nothing new

My feet hit the track
I don't look back
My yellow vest
Is ahead of the rest

I run with all my might
The finishing line is in sight
The race is over
I have won
Putting me in number one

I listen to the crowd
Their cheers are very loud
I am the fastest man alive!

Lucas Parsonage (11)
St George's College Weybridge, Addlestone

The Queen's Corgis

My name is Willow
I am a corgi
Not just a corgi
The Queen's corgi

I was adopted
When I was small
She took me home
And spoilt me more

Five of us live in the palace together
My friends were
Monty, Holly
Linnet and Emma

We slept on velvet
And ate the best food
They took us on walks
Through country and wood

My owner is special
Loving and kind
Queen or no queen
She will always be mine.

Riley Morris (12)
St George's College Weybridge, Addlestone

The Sketchbook

Oh dear, the next day begins
The child starts drawing on me and grins
It feels like another tattoo
His brother starts too
The brother is much worse, he presses so much harder
The child is so much smarter
These scars cut deep
As the pen does a sweep
My pages get more ink
It makes my heart sink
They love drawing
Even though it's like sawing
Away at my life.

John Carter (12)
St George's College Weybridge, Addlestone

Is Seeing Believing?

Pictures enter my mind, but not by colour and light
Standing at the shore, I'm comforted by the melodic sound
Of the tame waves as they tease my naked toes
I gulp a salty taste that my stomach does not welcome
I feel the heat of the sun gently caress my face
Leaving the hairs on my arms tingle
Although my eyes have imprisoned me
Satisfaction overwhelms.

Tara Burke (11)
St George's College Weybridge, Addlestone

Prison Problems

I am sat here in prison
After making a very bad decision
People always found it funny
That I grew up with no money
Still, I was told I had choices
But I did not listen to those voices
I went along to the shop and stole
Now I wait in my black hole
So here I am in prison
Due to my very silly decision.

Ollie Binns (11)
St George's College Weybridge, Addlestone

A Candle

I am a candle
I may be dull in the day
But at night, I shine bright
I am the nicest thing to light
I can bring happiness to you
But I can burn things down too
Don't squeeze my wick
Or I'll burn you quick.

Harvey Doran-Nesbitt (12)
St George's College Weybridge, Addlestone

Just Three Little Numbers

"Help!"
Knock! Knock!

"Help me! Please! Just someone, help!"
He bellowed
Knock! Knock! Knock!
No one opened up

The boy banged on the next door as he darted for his life
As the others chased after him
This was no joke
This was not a game
This was serious

As the people ran to their windows to see what all the
commotion was about
A deadly scene happened before their eyes

Still no help
No one called, no one opened up
And now those malicious boys that stabbed him in the chest
Were pointing and laughing at him

This was no laughing matter
A boy had just lost his life
He was only sixteen
And his parents totally oblivious
That their child that they'd seen a couple of hours ago
Was now gone

Not missing
Dead
Death is no joke

Three little numbers, that's all they had to press
Three little numbers could have meant that he could have
been happy and continuing his dream of being a footballer
Three little numbers, is that too much to ask?
If so, then why did they not open up?
But then again, this won't affect them
They don't care
They don't know him
Why should they be kind and not be selfish?
But it's only one person who this could affect
Surely his parents, family and friends don't care

Just three little numbers could have saved someone's life
Three little numbers would have made you a hero

All you had to dial was three little numbers.

Tarlan Mohammadi (13)
The Compton School, Finchley

The Day We Had To Leave...

The news was all about Brexit
But I did not know what that meant
They kept on saying, "Leave, leave, leave!"
But I also did not understand
I kept on asking myself, *what does this all mean?*
Until the next day
My mum and dad woke me up and said it was time to go
Go where? On holiday? To school? To Heaven?
All my parents said was to pack my clothes
We got on the bus to Golders Green
It was the most crowded day I have ever seen!
"Mum? Where are we going?" I asked
"We are going back to our country," my mum said in a sad
voice
I really did not understand
"We were already in our country," my mum said in a sad
voice
I really did not understand
We were already in our country
England is my home
It's where I go to school to see my friends
I did not know what to say back
"This is what Brexit is and this is how it will be from now on,"
said my dad
Now I know what Brexit is on the day I had to leave.

Rebeca Carvatchi (12)
The Compton School, Finchley

Gone Too Soon

From the moment I realised it was Alfie
My heart broke, I was scared
My heart was racing so fast, I couldn't breathe
He was my little boy and he was hurt
When he had his operation, I thought he was going to be okay
But then, when I saw him, my heart broke
My son, Alfie, tubes and machines
Nurses and doctors
I knew he wasn't coming home

Days passed, more scans, more operations
Nothing worked
My heart knew it was time to say goodbye and goodnight
The last time, my final farewell
He was in my arms when he took his last breath
At sixteen
The same way he took his first
Tears rolling down my cheek
I had to let him go with a stroke of his hair
And a kiss on his lips
I said

"Goodbye Alfie."

Scarlett Joanne Olivia Khan O'Keefe (11)
The Compton School, Finchley

My Body Judgement

All I had ever wanted was to fit in
But I didn't even know how to begin
So I asked my mum for the newest tech
My mum said no and I ended up a wreck
This boy in school wouldn't leave me alone
He would tease me and follow me as if he were my
shadow's clone
I cry and cry
Until both my eyes were swollen dry
I looked in the mirror to see what was wrong with me
But ribs and bones were all I could see
And then I realised that this is my body, not theirs
So I ignored everyone until no one else cared.

Melisa Shirvani (12)
The Compton School, Finchley

The Immigrant

I am hated, depressed
My present self cried
All I ever wanted was a better life
I sailed by the sea
To set myself free
Of course, I didn't want to leave the place
Where the air is filled with my childhood memories
Now I run from the darkened skies
And the piercing screams of the wounded
I am running but can still hear the innocent cries
I have come to a new land with no identity
Looked at as scum, kind words and smiles are seldom
If only they knew the price I had paid for my freedom.

Maryam Ahmed (12)
The Compton School, Finchley

Fifteen

Fifteen
Five ten
A number
A word
An age
An age of carefreeness
Freedom, vulnerability
The last chance to hold
Childhood's hand
Before you let go
Making it a mere memory of the past
A shadow period of your life
That stays with you
Forever
But when we move on
Grow, develop
Fifteen
Will just be
Five ten
A number
A word
An age.

Natalie Chu (16)
The Compton School, Finchley

Unrequited

It was the start of April
The cherry blossoms were in full bloom
As we were starting our first year in college
That was when I met you

At the time, I was a stranger
To the feeling described as love
No one warned me
About the devastating consequences

I wanted you
But you weren't mine to take
Even though I knew all of this
I sometimes wished you were

Badump! Badump! Badump!
Every time I tried to convince and tell myself
These feelings for you were just a mere mirage
My foolish heart pounded faster in your presence

It hurts, it hurts that
You don't feel the same way
It hurts that you like someone else
It hurts that you can't be mine

Of all the emotions I encountered
On this journey of self-exploration
Love was the most alluring
And painful feeling that I had ever felt.

Jasmine Kisembo Rahera (13)
The Urswick School, Hackney

Who Is To Be...?

They wonder
Wonder about their identity, their future, their image
But there's something we all wonder
About our feelings
They struggle on, admitting
Having feelings
But having feelings
Is as human as we get

It can be embarrassing
It can be emotional
It can be confusing
But they go through it
The most
As their bodies change
Their hearts change more
As they ask
"Who is to be...?"

Half of them are scared
So they treat it as nothing
And effect others for it
They worry over nothing and yet
These people get in the way of it
They fear being judged
But for what?
If they have found the one

They shouldn't fear but go on
Ahead
Everyone deserves a chance to feel

These people treat emotions as a game
Pressuring others to go their way
To go through the wrong door
To play the wrong card
They shouldn't let them
They go where they want to go
They play the card they want to play
They decide if they feel their emotions

These people assume that feelings are funny
They laugh at them and make people cry!
There's no reason why
But these people laugh and laugh at the people with
feelings
The people who feel, who can live, stay quiet
And that isn't a joke
Feelings aren't a joke
They connect us
Bond us
And they can make communities
So laugh at jokes, not at people's emotions

Feelings will lead our future
And that starts with them
But the prison of society says no

Society says no as if society can restrict us
Most of us have fallen victim to this plague
But they shouldn't
There shouldn't be any more wishes
For emotions
They shouldn't ask for permission
They should just feel

Their worries are illusions
Brought upon by those who fear
Emotions, they shouldn't
These are the most important years of their lives
And emotions are a key
To open one of the doors along the way
So, ignore those fears
Ignore the voice of society
Ignore those worries
And ask
Ask that important question in life
"Would you like to be...?"

Joe Owen (13)
The Urswick School, Hackney

Sexuality

Homophobia
It's not a phobia
It's just hate that came to us
Guided by bad luck and fate

"Yes, I'm gay," I said to my friend
"And my burning love for you will never end."
Then he held my hand
As we walked side by side

They turned and stared
As we passed them by
One of them shouted and
Told us to die

We went back to my house
He sat down and said
"Are we going to be okay?"
"Yes, we'll be fine."

So then and there
We got up, looking to face the world
We'd tell them who we were
And wouldn't be deterred

So here's a message
To all the boys and girls
Go out and show your pride
Let your voice be heard.

Lucas Narbrough (11)
The Urswick School, Hackney

Love, Racism And Equality

It's hard to love when the feeling isn't reciprocated
At least that's what she's learned
The relationship gets complicated
Then people watching from the sidelines get concerned

She's expected to turn a blind eye
She's expected not to be offended when she's been wronged
When people feel like they want to die
It seems like they're going beyond

Immaturity she despises
Not for her, they'll wear disguises
The guys around her are very incisive
Yet full of surprises

Switching the subject quickly
Some of the things mentioned are a bit tricky
But let's move on swiftly

Racism
Her skin tone is how you perceive her
Believe her
A lot of people want to be her
Whether she's black or white
She's not going to be uptight
Mixed race, light skin
She doesn't want to see any of this fighting

Don't differentiate because of race
There are rules we want to keep in place
Make this world a safe space
Equality is not meant to be chased

Many say life isn't a race
But if so, why are we chasing this money?
Why are we throwing out all the company?

She'd love to stick around and find out
Though the walls are closing in as she speaks
Once or twice, she might try and shout
But her voice isn't classed as unique

This is an outside perspective
She hasn't been through everything but feels the struggles
She wants to go against this as a collective
But she doesn't want to cause any rubble.

Miriam Hammond (12)
The Urswick School, Hackney

Future

The stars in the sky
Are shining brighter than ever
Trees dancing like butterflies
Nature is very clear

Wait a minute!

I see a blur in the distance
If we don't stop global warming in the next twelve years
I'll see you in Heaven

We must stop what we created
Or
In the end
We all will be devastated

You can't change the past
But there's always a future

A future that we can't predict
We try and evolve
But there's always a mist
A fog
We need to put an end to this
This
This isn't Harry Potter
To just say Avada Kedavra

Make a fresh new start
And don't blow away your choices to save nature

I'm present and I'm thinking about human beings
You're humans, you should be thinking about the future
How great the animals are
The pandas
The rhinos
The bees
To the elephants
And how they are becoming extinct
How great actually were they?
Future generations aren't going to experience their beauty
This is like the snap
But a lot more destructive
Because of us
We
We've been on this planet for a very short time
Let me convert it to the twenty-four-hour clock
Guess what?
We've been on Earth for three seconds
Is there even going to be a fourth?

Huseyin Kanli (12)
The Urswick School, Hackney

Fresh Print

The first feeling, the first touch
And the smell of the fresh print
Of this new book of mine
Full of meaning and words of wisdom
That could change lives forever

Any type of book is great
So long as it isn't a short book
Or a children's book
Or a book that has no meaning whatsoever
And that doesn't interest me at all

The book will interest me if it has an unexpected twist
If it has a little bit of spice
If it has romantic bits
And funny bits too
And a bit of adventure
All mixed together

If I could, I would have a library
Full of all the books I've ever read
And all my favourite books
And all the books I would like to read
I wouldn't be able to go a day without reading a book
Or at least having one with me or at home

I'm really grateful for books and literature
And having the ability to read and write

And learn about books
Thank you to all the poets and writers out there in the world
Never stop creating.

Valentina Hernandez Castrillon (13)

The Urswick School, Hackney

Phone

Turns on, breathes life
Dies and charges
It is happy

The image of being angelic is clear
The dark image no one hears
As useful as breathing
Still gleaming artificial sunlight

Sometimes someone would draw
Until it became a bore
Then gossip on social media
Because they were very lonely
And game and game
Overheating

Once stolen
Once confiscated
Once glitching
Once a small-screen crack
Phone worried

Software isolated, slow, sluggish
No one cares
Was the bestseller
Not
Feeling dark, it cries

More aggressive people became
Drop, fall, splash until it'd break
They abused it, they destroyed it
Barely living, paralysed

Man takes it
Mends and fixes
Sells it in a corner shop

Someone buys
At a price
Obsessive with the piece of tech
Started it on the same day

Years passed, data is old
So it gets transferred to a new body
The cycle starts again.

Alvin Ositelu (12)
The Urswick School, Hackney

The Immigrant's Backpack

Once I knew a beautiful place
The trees would sing, the wind played bass
Even the storms had a song they would sing
I fail to think of a more beautiful thing
Than this place

Once, I knew a small boy
To the huge, wild world, he was but a toy
He carried me on his back, I carried his book
When he saw a place, I would see the look
In his eyes

They twinkled like stars
They danced like a fire's heat
His black hair shone like the night
All of that time, I thought nothing could beat
The look in his eyes

Until that day

The bombs started falling
The walls started crumbling
The people started dropping
The food stopped coming
The trees stopped singing
The wind stopped playing
The storms started breaking
And with them, so did the look in his eyes

We had to flee
And all he took was his faithful backpack: me
The beautiful place disappeared in a sandstorm...

Esther Summers (12)
The Urswick School, Hackney

The Garden

A sprout of a stem
My own addition to the meticulous garden
My own emerald gem

I loved my little flower's first leaf
It came so suddenly
Without warning

You looked up at me, inspired
Summer sun shining on your pulchritudinous smile
Pink petals - so innocent

You were growing so fast
Your petals blossoming but you rejected my water and my light
And began to sink into darkness

Your complacency threatened me
I told you that we were in the clandestine garden now
Getting caught in the brambles

Now you have learnt
Now you are taller than the sunflowers and greater than the trees
You have experienced the vast garden

We are separate but, at heart, together
You no longer need me, but when your petals wither, just remember
I was there for you.

Noah Penton (14)
The Urswick School, Hackney

Life Of A Prisoner's Love

This is from the eyes of a prisoner
Thinking about all the days I had to eat this dinner
Has me thinking about
What I'm gonna do when I get out of here
Gotta change up the gears
To get my mind all clear

This prison isn't a tropical life
When you wanna sit back and drink those tropical vibes
Because you get into a fight and call a guard
Then they say, "Stay there
Till you leave to go to the yard."
So it's either lights out
Or find your way out

I wrote this letter saying
School is the place to be
So don't let anybody fool you
Choose your path correctly
Study your books
Don't let those girls fool you with those lies and good looks.

Jayden Greenaway-White (13)
The Urswick School, Hackney

The Foreigner

I'm a nobody without a name
A shameless lump of clay
I lie alone on the ground
Wishing I could levitate

New city, new school
I thought I wouldn't mind
But yet the people here
Are ruthless, mean and unkind

Yes I know I'm from a different place
Other than your own
Doesn't mean I'm a non-existent nobody
With 'non-human' written on my neck

It seems as if you want to hurt me
Want to see me suffer
But you don't even know me
My friends or family
Don't know my background
Nor my ethnicity

I'm the new kid in town
The different one
An outsider
I'm the foreigner.

Taejah Barrett (12)
The Urswick School, Hackney

The Day I Left My Family

The day I died was the day my whole family crumbled to
pieces
I could not stay another day to work, play, love
I wanted to help them, but I couldn't
I was in pieces

A lot happened since my death
It shattered me inside
One of my daughters joined me
Three of my children got married
And I've had many more grandchildren
If my parting has left a hole in your heart
Fill it with joy and happiness

Day after day, I watch my family come
To look over my grace
Nothing makes me happier than that
I watch the tears tremble down their faces
It hurts
Deep down, I want to help them
They're in pieces
It hurts.

Alesha Hoque (13)
The Urswick School, Hackney

Colours Dancing In The Light

I see fire burning in my mind
The red, amber and yellow come to life
Dancing colours in the light
The contrast between green and red
The smoke above it rising

Painful embers sparking in the light
The green set alight, the red catching up with me
I try to get away
The wind brushes against my face
As I run across the ground
The red catching up with me
I trip, stumble, fall

Nothing
Suddenly, in a moment, it all comes down
Like a wave crashing onto me
I look up, my vision blurred
All I see are dots of red and yellow, dancing in the light.

Jude McCaughren (13)
The Urswick School, Hackney

A Father's Heart

A father's heart must be strong
True as the stones Earth was made from
My child's eyes, innocent
Yet an ocean of mischief and curiosity

A father's heart must be wise
Big as the moon shining down
My child's love, it flows from her like water
Kindness abound and wondrous

A father's heart must give in
Know when it's time for the white flag
My child's happiness, incredible
Sinful thought, to imprison and bind joy

A father's heart for my child
For her to carry into the sun.

Sudenaz Top (15)
The Urswick School, Hackney

YOUNG WRITERS
INFORMATION

We hope you have enjoyed reading this book – and that you will continue to in the coming years.

If you're a young writer who enjoys reading and creative writing, or the parent of an enthusiastic poet or story writer, do visit our website **www.youngwriters.co.uk**. Here you will find free competitions, workshops and games, as well as recommended reads, a poetry glossary and our blog. There's lots to keep budding writers motivated to write!

If you would like to order further copies of this book, or any of our other titles, then please give us a call or order via your online account.

Young Writers
Remus House
Coltsfoot Drive
Peterborough
PE2 9BF
(01733) 890066
info@youngwriters.co.uk

Join in the conversation!
Tips, news, giveaways and much more!

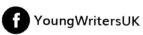 YoungWritersUK    @YoungWritersCW